HIT BY A LOW-FLYING GOOSE
AND OTHER CAUTIONARY
TALES

NOTES FROM THE LIFE AND PRACTICE
OF A PEDIATRICIAN AND HIS WIFE

BY JOHN GALL, MD, FAAP, AND CAROL GALL

To Bonnie –

This will introduce you to me,
and probably some things new to you
about John. My chapters are signed.
Hes are not. Enjoy!

Carol

GENERAL SYSTEMANTICS PRESS
WALKER, MINNESOTA

2

Library of Congress Control Number:

Library of Congress Cataloging in Publication Data:

Gall, John C., and Carol A. Gall

Hit by a Low-flying Goose and Other Cautionary Tales: Notes From the Life and Practice of a Pediatrician and his Wife. By John C. Gall and Carol A. Gall

Gall, John, 1925—

Gall, Carol, 1944—

ISBN: 978-0-9618251-8-8

Published by: The General Systemantics Press,
7027 S. Walker Bay Road, NW, Walker, MN 56484

Web site: www.generalsystemantics.com

TABLE OF CONTENTS

4

6

PREFACE

A pediatrician's life is not all smiles. True, there are lighter moments, but many episodes are ambiguous, even dark. We (the authors) hope you will find these stories interesting, but our primary goal is to make you think about them. They are intended as teaching tales. The moral to be drawn from some of them is simply that *life is like that*, not always Utopian, and that we need to recognize the facts on the ground. For other stories, there are other conclusions, harder to see and perhaps even harder to acknowledge, assimilate, and learn from. If these stories stimulate you to think, then they have achieved their purpose. If you enjoy reading them, then we have achieved a double satisfaction.

All the stories in this collection (except for one or two, where known public figures are intentionally named) have been edited to prevent identification while preserving their essential truthfulness. In some cases two or more individuals have been coalesced in order to preserve anonymity.

A & D OINTMENT[1]

To fail to recognize a serious disease is a shame to the physician and a disaster for the patient and his family. To fail to recognize a raging epidemic is a catastrophe for the entire society and a shame to the entire healing profession.

When I was a medical student and intern and later a resident in Pediatrics, way back in the nineteen-fifties, there was a very strange disease called "spontaneous fractures of infancy." A lot of time was spent in serious speculation about what sort of metabolic disorder could result in spontaneous fractures of the long bones, spontaneous fractures of the skull, spontaneous bleeding over the surface of the brain. I remember seeing a one-year old child hospitalized on the pediatric ward with simultaneous spontaneous fractures of both legs, and I wondered what sort of metabolic disease could produce effects like that.

Many times a baby would be admitted for some illness such as pneumonia, and X-rays of the chest would reveal what really looked very much like healing of the long bones, the arm bones, the rib bones, the kind of healing that would occur after a fracture.

Such babies would be sent home after they got over their pneumonia, only to be readmitted a week later or a month later with collections of fluid over the brain, just as if they were recovering from some sort of injury to the head. When I went into my residency and later, when I was practicing at a well-known medical center, we would see such patients and wonder just what sort of mysterious disease it was that could produce such strange effects.

It wasn't until a young radiologist by the name of Caffey looked straight into the eyes of the monster and called it by its true name, that we began to understand that we were seeing battered children. And even then, it took another thirty years

---

1 From *Elegant Parenting*, 1994

for helping professionals everywhere to realize that child abuse is not some rare and esoteric event, but a thing that is with us every day, and a terrible reality for a substantial percentage of the world's children.

Freud had stumbled upon this fact when he realized how many of his clients gave histories of parental seduction or parental abuse or both. But as the evidence accumulated, he shrank back from acknowledging that so high a percentage of children could have been actually physically abused by their parents. He retreated into a theory that the abuse occurred in the fantasy life of the children and not in actual fact. And this is the historical background for the strange fact that it was not the psychiatrists of the world who made us aware of child abuse, but a radiologist. Some enlightened psychiatrists understood, but most of them were busy confirming Freud's assertion that it was not real child abuse, but the child's fantasy of being abused, that was the basic cause of mental disorder.

I regard the effects of abusive parenting as the Number One chronic handicapping disease of children in the world today.

By and large people do not procreate children with the deliberate intention of abusing them. But they have been raised in a certain way, they have a certain set of attitudes, they have a certain repertoire for dealing with situations, and that repertoire is what they themselves learned as children. So when they have tried their repertoire and they still have a screaming child or a fussy baby, or when the baby won't eat or the toddler keeps running away, they revert to what was done to them in similar circumstances. It's a matter of unconscious learnings from the distant past. And when they strike their child, or shake their baby, this behavior is a surprise to them. They don't know where that behavior of theirs came from. They don't remember what was done to them.

The remedy for this is preventive. A parent must have sufficient repertoire, must have a large enough bag of tricks, to be able to produce desired results. And part of this is in knowing what a baby is capable of—what a baby can be expected to be able to do and what is the parent's responsibility. And the time to start this preparation is before the baby is born.

Three-year-old Eric really had his parents upset. They were old-fashioned disciplinarians who believed in spanking, but they also tried to be enlightened and use time-outs first. They had sent Eric to his room for some misbehavior, and Eric had taken a one-pound jar of sticky, smelly A&D ointment and smeared it all over the four walls of his room, as high as he could reach. Mother discovered you can't wash A&D ointment off with a washcloth, it won't come off with detergent, you can't even scrape it off because it soaks through the wallpaper and even into the drywall. They had to have Eric's room completely redone from the walls out. And they were afraid of what they might do to Eric if he continued his misbehavior. So they agreed to come to the parenting class that my wife and I conducted every other Saturday.

Father came, too, dressed in a blue pinstripe business suit complete with vest and tie and watch chain. And he made it clear that as a business executive and a reserve officer in the military, no one was going to take away his right as a citizen to discipline and to spank his own child in the privacy of his own home.

We agreed completely. We were not there to limit him in his options. We merely wanted to offer him a broader range of options, some of which might offer him a better chance of success in guiding his son along the right path.

And they stayed and listened and thanked us and went home and they didn't come back to the next class, and my late wife Beth and I reminded ourselves that you can't win 'em all, if they don't stay to learn you can't blame yourself for that.

But then they did come back, a month later. Dad reported that they had missed the previous class because his own father had died and he had gone to the funeral, and at the funeral he realized he couldn't even cry for the death of his father, because he kept remembering the spankings and the mean, cruel things his father had done to punish him when he was only a little kid. A wave of determination swept over him that he didn't want Eric ever to feel that way about him. As he told us this, in the class, he broke down and cried. And they stayed for the whole series of classes.

Five years later, when Eric was almost nine years old, Beth met them socially and asked if the classes had been helpful.

Mom replied: "Oh, we never had a chance to try out the things you taught us. After that episode with the A&D ointment, he changed so completely that we never had to spank him again."

As helping professionals you understand that when people change, they must interpret that change to themselves in a way that makes sense to them. When you have really made a change in a person's life, don't expect them necessarily to realize that you did it. It may not seem like that to them at all.

A BLACK WIDOW BITE[2]

I took my pediatric training at the Mayo Clinic way back in the days when it was called a Fellowship, not a residency. I had just completed a brutal internship, where failure to perform up to standards could result in peremptory dismissal and the end of one's career in medicine, and so I showed up promptly at 7 AM on my first day wearing a clean, starched white coat. The attending physician stared at my coat; then he did something that shocked me and changed my life and attitude forever. He reached out his hand and shook mine and said, "Dr. Gall, I'm Haddow Keith. Welcome to the Mayo Clinic. We're all licensed physicians here, so you don't need to wear any kind of uniform, just your everyday jacket."

I felt ten feet tall. All of us in the program did, too. We were going to be treated like human beings. We strove to be worthy of that status of equality that had been conferred on us. In fact, we strove so hard that in a year or two we began to think we really were the equals of those gods of medicine. Then I encountered something that shook me to the core.

A little 8-year-old boy had been brought into the hospital late the night before with what looked for all the world like epileptic seizures. A look of terror came over his face, he sat bolt upright in the bed, stiffened, jerked convulsively, then shrank back and tried to bury himself in the pillow. After a few minutes he would recover enough to sit up again.

He had been sent for an emergency brain wave test that showed some type of spike-like abnormalities, but no true epileptic pattern. The neurologist had done an emergency neurological exam and found no abnormality.

The nurse who had been with him all night reported that she had finally been able to make sense of his shrieks. A giant black widow spider six feet tall would suddenly appear in the

2 Presented at *Under Fire: Childhood in the Shadow of War.* The Cotsen Conference, Princeton, NJ, October 11, 2005.

room and lunge at him, trying to bite him and kill him.

So what were we seeing? Early-onset schizophrenia? Some bizarre form of epilepsy or some sort of hallucinatory panic reaction or what? How would the great Mayo Clinic respond to this utterly unclassifiable mystery?

Then the social worker came into the room.

(I might comment that this is what made the Mayo Clinic so great. Where else in the world could you get a neurologist, an electroencephalographer, and a social worker to show up at 2 AM and work for six hours straight to solve a non-life-threatening emergency problem that no one could understand?)

The boy's mother was living alone in an isolated farmhouse. Her husband had deserted her, it was midwinter in Minnesota, she didn't know how she was going to feed her three children. She began to believe enemies were surrounding her home and flashing lights into her eyes to confuse her. She gathered her three children together and ran with them through the snow to the barn, where she thought she might be safe. (This was in the days of the so-called "Cold War".)

The nearest neighbors saw the commotion and drove over to help her. Their headlights made beams in the icy fog, and the mother thought the CIA and the Communists had finally come to kill them all. At least she could protect her children by killing them before they could be captured. She had already killed two of them before the neighbors ran up and stopped her.

Our 8-year-old patient was being strangled by his own mother when they rescued him.

And now here he was, being persecuted by fantasies of a giant black widow spider trying to kill him. Fate had forced into his conscious awareness one of those fantasies that for the sake of sanity must remain forever unconscious—the image of the devouring mother.

The Mayo Clinic responded beautifully to such a challenge back in those primitive days of the 1950's. They didn't medicate the little boy, they didn't treat him as if he had a disease; they provided him with support and security and a chance to tell his story over and over, day after day, until he was able in some way to assimilate what had happened to him.

That was the day on which I learned that I didn't know it all, I didn't know anything. I didn't even know the name of the game I was trying to play, or the rules. That little boy haunted me for decades until I finally decided to make the break from academic medicine and go into practice on my own and try to learn how to understand what's really going on in this world.

A MATTER OF TASTE

Babies have very sensitive taste buds and can detect tiny variations in flavor and texture of their food. They are quite capable of reacting to even such seemingly-insignificant factors as the difference in rate of milk flow in one breast as compared to the other, or even tiny variations in nipple size and location that require the baby to make slight postural adjustments.

As one mother put it, "He's in love with my left breast."

She was a very maternal young mother who loved to breast feed her new baby boy. When he began pulling away, making faces, and refusing to nurse, she was heartbroken. She came for consultation with my late wife, Beth, and Beth systematically reviewed with her the possible causes of nipple rejection. Dietary changes? Onions, cabbage, any other suspect foods? No. Nipple ointments, lotions? No. Nipple discharge, mastitis? No. Any upsetting family changes? No. Was Mom pregnant again? No. Baffled, Beth asked if she could come in again the next day, to give Beth time to review her printed sources and to think about the problem.

"Could I come back tomorrow afternoon? I've just started up again with my neighborhood swimming group, and we meet tomorrow morning."

The light dawned. Beth said, "Take a full thirty-minute shower after your swim. Lather up three times and rinse thoroughly."

Mom returned the next afternoon to report the problem was solved. Her baby didn't like the taste of chlorine!

A REALLY CRAZY MOM

Now, Fiona was really crazy. I didn't know that at first, when she brought her new baby to me at the office for baby checkups and shots. She was a sad single mother whose husband had died in a traffic accident several months ago, leaving her to bear their first and only child alone. Her plain round Irish face was red with weeping.

She had what I considered to be an Irish willfulness or stubbornness, and a belligerence that I thought was a cover for her grief.

That was all I thought until I got a call from the social service agency. The worker in charge of child abuse problems was saying that Fiona had been reported to their agency by a neighbor who had heard Fiona yelling out terrible threats at her little baby, threatening to do bodily harm to the infant in her crib if she didn't stop crying.

The social worker (his name was Brian) said they had checked with Fiona's psychiatrist and had found out that she was schizophrenic: they were planning to take custody of the baby for its own safety. They were calling to ask if I had any additional information that might be pertinent.

And I heard myself replying, almost as if musing to myself:

"She loves her child, it's the one precious thing she has. She has already lost her husband. Her family just want to get rid of her. If you take away her child, she really will go crazy and you will have to put her in a locked ward forever after. You will kill her."

John, what are you saying? If this woman hurts her child, you will be held responsible!

Long pause. Then Brian (bless his Irish heart!) speaks again.

"Then you will be willing to assume responsibility for the baby's safety?"

"Yes. I'll be responsible."

I put the phone down shakily. What had I let myself in for?

Fiona brought the baby to me at the proper times for checkups and shots, and the baby grew and thrived. Fiona never did any violence to her baby. She grumbled, she blamed the baby, to hear her talk was to be shaken by the irrational violence in her tone, but she never hurt her baby. It was all talk—really ugly talk, but just talk. The baby just smiled and basked in the angry rumble and roar of her mother's voice.

Fiona knew that the social work people had been thinking of taking away her baby and that her baby-doctor had stopped them, or at least held them off during good behavior on her part. Fiona at one point said darkly that if they took her baby away she'd kill herself for sure. Or kill somebody.

Fiona's manner was belligerent. She did a lot of complaining. She didn't like people very much. She didn't have many friends. She wasn't even very friendly to her baby-doctor but continued to bring her growing child to me and to follow the advice she was given for earaches and colds and the many little illnesses of childhood.

But she also called me up at night on the telephone from her single apartment on the other side of town, and those phone calls were disturbing and scary. Her tone was loud and angry. It wasn't always clear what she was upset about. Sometimes it was the neighbors; sometimes it was her willful child; sometimes her pets, the dog, the cat, the parrot, were misbehaving. Her parents, living in a distant city, were conspiring to take away her daughter, were trying to drive her crazy. She would get louder and louder until she was shouting full force into the telephone. I would yell back, telling her to stop agitating.

"I gotta hang up now, the damn police are at the door. The neighbors have called the police."

Sometimes she would call back afterwards to tell me the police had told her to quiet down and stop disturbing her neighbors.

The phone calls and the visits to the office seemed to keep some thread of human communication intact for her. Baby Serena was now a bright, exploring toddler with a smiling round Irish face and a gift for making friends. She was clearly thriving while in the care of a disturbed, lonely single mother.

Fiona started bringing the child in to the office unannounced. She would show up at lunchtime when my late wife Beth and I were in the back room having our lunch. It seemed only natural and humane to offer them some soup, a sandwich.

Fiona was a strict disciplinarian, almost a martinet.

"Eat your soup!"

"Don't dawdle!"

"Don't slurp your soup!"

The critical comments, the peremptory orders, seemed to come out automatically. Using all her diplomatic skills, Beth tried to demonstrate how to interact in a more positive way. It was hard to tell if Fiona understood what Beth was trying to show her. Fiona would launch into long angry tirades about how ungrateful children are; it was hard to keep her on a specific point.

She was an angry, truculent, argumentative, stubborn woman with a loud, angry voice and a generally unlikable manner.

But she kept coming back. Even worse, she began wandering into the front office, offering to help file charts and do paperwork. She did it in such an intrusive and offensive manner, getting in the way of the front-office people, that Beth and I had to confront her and make her stop even as we realized Fiona was trying to do something to pay us back for the endless hours we were spending on this forlorn little couple.

It was gratitude, expressed in such a way as almost to guarantee a negative reaction. Finally, she stayed out of the front office but continued to come to lunch and hang around the office for hours at a time.

Fiona did have a job, sometimes. She did something with theater lights. And she worked—sometimes—as a movie projectionist, keeping the twin projectors running properly during the showing of the movies. She often grumbled about the hours, the pay scale, the lack of regular work.

She was also a photographer. That is, she had a little snapshot camera and took pictures of things that interested her. She brought little prints for Beth and me to see—shots of tall marsh grass, tangled stems woven together, no detectable composition to the pictures, almost unrecognizable, just tangles of dead grass. A close-up of the empty window of an abandoned barn, looking like a baleful eye.

She also did paintings: zigzags of primary colors, totally abstract, repellent, depressing.

One day at lunch she announced:

"I'm not going back to that psychiatrist any more. All he does is tell me to keep taking my prescriptions."

"You're taking medication?"

"Every day, just like he says."

"What's it for?"

"My hallucinations."

"You have hallucinations?"

"I hear voices all the time."

"When did they start?"

"Before my baby was born."

"Does the medicine help?"

"Not a damn bit. Well, it makes the voices a little fainter."

"Then why do you keep taking it?"

"The doc says I'm supposed to. Can I come see you instead? At least you talk to me."

A quick decision. Beth and I glance at each other.

"I'll take you on, on two conditions. First, you must promise to take my advice and do whatever I recommend, no back talk. OK?"

"OK." Fiona is looking interested, intrigued.

"Second, you have to gather up all your medications and flush them down the toilet. No exceptions. Cold turkey. No more meds."

Fiona doesn't hesitate. This second condition appeals to her rebellious, contrary part.

"OK."

Fiona, bringing Serena along, continued to show up as usual for lunch two or three times a week. As usual, she dominated the conversation with her grumbling and complaining, and nobody could get a word in edgewise. It was three weeks before I could ask her, point blank:

"What about your voices?"

"Oh, they're gone."

"Gone? When did they stop?"

"I don't know exactly. A couple of weeks ago."

That was the last of the voices.

I remember scheduling Fiona for hour-long sessions. In my own mind they were a lost cause. Fiona dominated the conversation, spent the hour angrily denouncing the evils and shortcomings of the world around her, her neighbors, her employers. Nevertheless, she kept coming back. I ordered her to attend the parenting seminars that I and Beth conducted every Sunday afternoon. She didn't seem to pay any attention to the idea of strategic parenting, just went off on long tangents about how ungrateful and sneaky children can be. Not for Fiona the idea of taking notes, of studying assigned texts, of practicing specific interactions! She just kept blasting away in that foghorn voice of hers, finding fault with the whole world.

Nevertheless, she kept coming back.

Her paintings were changing. She was now painting recognizable objects, a pitcher of drinking water, a landscape with farm buildings. Her snapshots were changing also: a local pond with weeping willows hanging down close to the water, the fronds mirrored in the still water.

Slowly, she began to tell what had happened to her.

Expelled from her wealthy social-climbing family for marrying someone they disapproved of, she tried to build a cocoon of love involving just the two of them, living on his tiny earnings in a tiny apartment in town. After a few months she came home radiant from the doctor to tell him she was pregnant. Without a word he jumped on his bicycle and rode downtown into the traffic and was killed. Her world fell apart.

She called me on the phone in the middle of the day.

"When am I gonna be cured?"

"You can't be cured, Fiona, because you don't have a disease."

Long silence.

"You mean I have to do it myself?"

"Yes."

You, Fiona, the victim, the abused one, now have to climb the dangerous mountain of the comeback trail, undoing what was done to you. There's no justice; you can't make the offenders, the criminals, do this for you. Precisely because you are the victim, you must also do the hard work of recovering. The neglected, abused infant must now learn how to comfort herself.

And it gets worse. The defenses you learned as a child, to protect yourself, the protective attitude you took upon yourself, are now your worst enemy. Your truculent, belligerent approach drives people away. People don't like being approached as if they were enemies.

Her parents hadn't wanted her. A baby interfered with their life style. She was raised by a succession of nannies. In school she was brilliant, gifted in art and literature. It didn't matter. Her parents still didn't like her. They wanted her out of the line of succession to the family fortune. When she began misbehaving, they found psychiatrists to put the stigma of mental illness on her. When she ran away, they closed ranks and barred her from returning. By then she was alienated, disaffected, didn't want to return anyway.

She was driven mad by bad luck and by the cold and calculating cruelty of her selfish parents.

It came out piecemeal, the way it happened, over a period of years. With each revelation, she raged and grieved, got worse, then a little better than before.

Five years have gone by. Her little daughter, now in kindergarten, is gifted in art and language, produces happy drawings for her doctor.

Ten years go by, then fifteen. The daughter has a boy friend, they are planning to get married. Fiona helps them.

She welcomes the child that is her grandchild.

How do you define the word "cure?" What do you mean by the word, "schizophrenia"?

I discussed the case with an eminent University Professor.

"She didn't have schizophrenia," he said. "Schizophrenia is incurable, and she got better, so she didn't have it."

I agreed with him that she didn't have "schizophrenia." She merely had some of the *symptoms* of schizophrenia, and now she didn't.

A YEAR AHEAD OF HIMSELF

Our older son entered kindergarten a year ahead of schedule. It was the 1960's—things like that happened. When he got to high school, we told him, "You are a year ahead of yourself, so when you graduate from high school, you can have a free year to do anything you want to do before going to college."

He chose to tour Europe with the Youth for Understanding band. He played with the band in several European capitals and had a wonderful time. Then, on the train in Yugoslavia, his passport was stolen and he was taken away by the secret police, whisked on a plane to Belgrade, and interrogated. We only knew that he had disappeared and that we couldn't contact him. We were frantic.

He was released to rejoin his group. When he returned, he was a mature young man, ready to go to college. He knew the value of a college education.

ACTIVE WAITING

Carol Gall

For about ten years I took in young men who for one reason or another had nowhere else to go. The term "street kids" had not yet been coined, but that is the category into which they would fall today. I made few rules for them, really only three: (1) no swearing in my presence (2) no drinking or drugs in the house (3) if anyone got into trouble outside of my house, they were on their own to get out of whatever they had gotten into. In addition, of course, each child had to notify their parent or parents as to where they were, I had to talk to the parents and get an address and phone number for them, and the child had to both enroll in school and attend.

It actually worked out quite well. Most of the young men, if not all, had had little effective guidance about their behaviors and their consequences and were prone to make mistakes, some of which could have had long-term consequences for their lives. Put several kids like that together, and an interesting phenomenon occurred. They told on one another! So I usually found out what was going on, or what they were contemplating doing, which allowed some of these potentially destructive behaviors to be headed off at the pass, so to speak.

My own children are adopted, and are African American. (I am Swedish.) They came as older children, so had emotional baggage of their own. It was useful for them to be able to be helpful to young men who had had less guidance than they had. I overheard one of my boys say to a new boy on his first day in our home, "Don't ever lie to my Mom. She always knows. We don't know *how* she knows, but she always knows. So don't ever lie to my Mom!"

At one point I had several extra boys besides my own two living in our small home. All of them were concerned about Tommy. Tommy had come to the house in the early spring. He had just graduated from high school the previous school year, so he was at home during the day. In fact, he was home during the morning, afternoon, and evening, every morning, every afternoon, and every evening! He never ventured outside of the house. He didn't even want to take our dog, Kelly, outside, and I didn't require him to.

The other boys were sure there was a warrant out for his arrest. They thought we should call the police and check. I said, "I don't really think so. I think something else is going on. But if there is a warrant out for him, the police will eventually find him."

Tommy didn't venture out all summer. The boys tried to entice him to go with them to events they thought he would enjoy. Once they even pooled their money to buy him a ticket to the rock concert they had saved their money for, but he wouldn't "budge his butt," as the other boys put it.

One late summer day, I made breakfast for Tommy. The other boys happened to be gone, so it was just Tommy and I in the house. We were sitting at the breakfast table.

Tommy said, "May I talk to you?"

"Sure," I replied. "What's up?"

Tommy said, "I was sexually abused since I was six years old by the man who lived next door to me until I came to live here. I would like to call the police and tell them about it."

"Oh, Tommy," I said, "I'm so sorry! But reporting it isn't as easy as it seems. The police will interrogate you and you may feel that they are not on your side. They may treat you as if *you* have done something wrong. If they decide to arrest the man, you will have to go to court and face questioning by the man's lawyer. Are you sure you are up for all of that? It is likely to be very difficult to go through!"

"Yes, I want to report this!" Tommy was sure.

He made the phone call. The man was arrested, successfully prosecuted, and jailed. And Tommy went outside again.

All of this occurred when I was a single parent and when my own boys were teen-agers, in the middle eighties.

In 1994 I married my present husband and worked with him in his office.

One morning one of our first appointments was a fourteen-year-old boy who had come into the office to receive a booster shot of some sort. He arrived at the appointed time, but once there, he didn't want to receive the shot.

My husband said to the boy, "Why don't you go into the waiting room and think about it? You can let me know when you are ready."

The boy went into the waiting room and sat. And sat. And sat. The nurse practitioner tried to convince us that he was being a "sissy" and should just be ordered to come in and get that shot over with!

"Why are you pandering to a sissy?" she wanted to know. "It's absolutely beyond me why you are letting this boy act so silly!"

We didn't answer her, but let the boy sit there. My husband, noticing that the boy was softly crying, asked him if he would like to sit in the back room. He said he would.

He didn't get his shot that day. He came in three weeks later and received it without incident. And when he did, he announced sadly that his parents had filed for divorce the day before.

Sometimes the best solution to a problem is active waiting. There is wisdom in allowing events to unfold in their own time.

AFRAID OF SCHOOL PHOBIA

Amelia was twelve years old, a tall, intelligent girl who was an excellent student at school. She came down with the flu in October of that year. Her parents had just separated and were thinking seriously of divorce. She was quite ill for six weeks. She developed virus pneumonia and continued to be excessively fatigued and weak for several weeks more.

Her mother, to avoid the possibility of a relapse, quite properly kept her home until her strength should come back to normal. But Amelia caught another cold and had to stay home another two weeks, and after that she just couldn't seem to get her strength back. This went on for three whole months.

Finally the school nurse contacted me and told me she thought Amelia had school phobia (separation anxiety) and reminded me of my duty as Amelia's pediatrician to follow the recommendation of the most eminent psychiatric authorities, which is that children with school phobia must be returned to school as soon as possible in order to prevent the problem from becoming chronic and intractable.

I saw Amelia and her mother the next day. After examining Amelia and ascertaining that she had no significant illness, I turned to her mother and told her, in Amelia's presence, that she was under no circumstances to allow Amelia to go to school on any day when she, the mother, was not completely convinced that Amelia was well, and that in order to be absolutely certain of this, she was to examine Amelia thoroughly first thing every morning, taking her temperature if need be, and only if Amelia passed inspection was she to be allowed to go to school.

Then I turned to Amelia and I said, "You know, over there at the school, they think you've got School Phobia!"

When Amelia heard this, her face turned pale, her eyes blinked rapidly, and she began to breathe faster. I immediately told her mother to take her home and not send her back to school until she was sure she was well.

It was several months later before I again had a contact from Amelia's mother. She reported that Amelia had insisted on going back to school that very afternoon, had indignantly refused to let her mother examine her in the mornings, had kept a perfect attendance record for the rest of the year, was class valedictorian and had starred in the class play.

And the divorce? Yes, that had gone through but Amelia seemed more concerned about whether she might have to miss any school on that account. I also got a letter from the school nurse verifying that Amelia had, indeed, missed only one day of school since her visit to the office.

A followup four years later revealed that Amelia was a senior in high school, a valued member of the track team, and a Merit Scholar.

Her cure was, first, to be required to submit to her mother's physical exam every day, and, second, her fear that her classmates might think she was afraid to go to school.

The total cost for this intervention was twenty-eight dollars, the cost of a routine twelve-minute office visit to the pediatrician. Pediatricians in our community were paid on the assumption that they could see and adequately deal with one patient every twelve minutes. My fee was not covered by insurance because it was only an office visit, and there was no charge for psychotherapy or counseling because no diagnosis of mental disorder was ever made. And besides, the HMO central office has fits when a pediatrician tries to charge for counseling. But Amelia has no mental health dossier to follow her around for the rest of her life. And I do believe that a person in any of the helping professions has one and only one cardinal duty, and that is to do what is best for their patient, even if other people don't understand.

AGE MATTERS[3]

Age is very important to a child. You can start an interaction with a two-year-old by asking:

"Are you two?"

You will most likely get an answer like:

"Two years old."

Or, "I'm two."

They say it in a special kind of singsong that tells you it's still just verbal, they don't really have the concept of time, but you have made them feel important just by asking; and they feel competent just by being able to answer you. So it's a very satisfying interaction. You have told them they are important and competent without ever using those big words. You only asked them, "Are you two?"

With a three year old, there's often a big difference.

"I'm tha-ree years old."

You can hear the pride in their tone of voice. What they are saying is, "That's who I am."

It's a matter of identity. You are validating their identity.

With four, five, six, seven, it's different again. It's a matter of achievement, of status. They are older than mere three-year-olds.

Now, with a girl:

"Are you nine years old?"

"Oh, yes."

"Are you nine years and six months?"

You can see the sudden blink, the quick inward search, the mental calculation.

---

3 From *Dancing with Elves*, 2000

"Yeeaah." There's puzzlement. What is this all about?

"Are you nine years and six months and four days old?"

Blank smile, laugh of puzzlement.

"You mean you don't know how old you are?! It's time for you to start keeping track of these things!"

What does she think? She thinks, "He says I need to know how old I am. I have to start keeping track of such things."

What things? The calendar, of course.

"I have to start keeping track of the calendar."

What is this all about?

It's about girls learning to keep track of the calendar, the days of the month. It's the beginning of sex education, without a single word being said about sex.

No embarrassment at all. We're only talking about how old she is, a topic of great interest to her.

AN AGENDA-LESS AGENDA

By Carol A. Gall

It was a balmy October day, the kind of day when the season seems at one moment to be summer and at the next moment to be fall. The sun shone brightly for a few minutes, but shortly, clouds overtook the entire sky. The temperature fell. The clouds released their moisture only lightly one minute, but poured rain the next, after which the sun brightly overtook all and it became warm again.

I was driving home from the grocery store on a rural road, three miles or so in length, tree lined at the beginning and at the end. The middle of the drive had a clearing with a pond to the left, with many waterfowl of various types. The birds looked serene. No one bothered them there, and it seemed they were conscious of and appreciated their privacy.

It was my favorite sort of road, in that there was seldom any traffic. Today there was none. I could drive with my mind turned off, so to speak, basking in the beauty of the day, not worrying about holding up anyone who fancied that the few seconds they would save by speeding was worth the effort or the jangled, tangled nervous system that ensues.

When I neared the end of the small drive, I saw that the leaves had given up their summer green but not too many of them had turned brown and fallen as they had in other spots in our area. I became aware of the intense yellows, oranges, and deep, deep reds in the foliage, and without volition on my part, saw the trees seem to lean towards me as if showing me the very best of themselves. My eyes became misty. What an honor to behold such a sight and to sense the giving of these "beings" of the vegetable kingdom!

I have been privileged many times in my life to experience the best of what some being has to give. In the morning I had met four boys for their first piano lessons with me as their teacher after studying a year with another teacher in another small town. All four of them in turn had leaned forward at the piano, coaxing out the best tones and most accurate rendering of the musical notation in front of them that their ability and prior training would allow. Was I listening? They saw that I *was* and that *I liked their music* and in that wordless communication a flowering occurred, and a setting of mutual admiration was established both for the day and for the future.

It is like that in teaching. It is like that in nature. It is like that in pediatrics. It is like that in life. It happens when there is an agenda-less agenda. It happens when one appreciates what is there.

AN EMERGENCY SKIN RASH

Carol Gall

My husband John once told me that he had been invited, as a medical student, to consider a career in Dermatology. Skin patients, he was told, never die, never get well, and never need night calls.

One morning I decided to go into the office early to work on paperwork for the HMO's. The words of my husband were ringing in my ears: "I don't want my wife doing clerical work!" I didn't care for the idea either; I *did,* however, wish us to be paid for the services my husband had rendered, and that meant paperwork, piles and piles of paperwork to be done if we wished to be reimbursed.

On a whim I decided to cancel the answering service at 7 a.m. when I arrived, instead of waiting for the usual eight o'clock turn-over. I didn't really expect any calls, and if I got any, I could always page my husband on his pager, or call the hospital, where he was checking on a newborn baby, if there was anything I couldn't handle. I thought perhaps as it got close to eight o'clock, people might begin calling for the day's appointments. Often mothers who had been up all night with a child crying with an earache would rush to the phone at the first possible moment they thought our office might answer the phone.

"How boring!" I thought to myself as I got out the thick file of claims needing attention. The HMO's seemed to find any of a thousand reasons to deny a legitimate claim, for reasons all the way from forgetting to fill in the ending date of service (in our office the beginning and ending date of service were the same 99% of the time, as our patients were rarely hospitalized under our care) to a demand for more information.

Just how much was there to say about a positive strep throat culture and the administration of an antibiotic, I wondered from time to time, as a certain percentage of routine procedures were routinely denied coverage. Were they just rejecting certain claims for no reason, thinking that some practitioners were too overwhelmed with paperwork to re-file these rejected claims? There was a time limit, 90 days from the date of service, for all claims to be in their office with all the i's dotted and the t's crossed, so time was of the essence. It *did* happen at times that their deadline came and went without our re-filing, so that the chance for reimbursement was lost. That was, in fact, why I was there, to finish the work needed to submit claims that were getting close to the deadline.

At about five minutes after seven the telephone rang. A man was on the line, calling about his daughter, aged fourteen. I asked him to hold the line while I quickly fetched this child's file.

"What is the problem?" I asked.

"She has been awake all night, screaming," he declared flatly. His tone indicated no alarm.

"Is she in pain?" I asked. "Why is she screaming?"

He replied, again flatly, "She has psoriasis."

I thought to myself, "Psoriasis! Why would anyone be screaming because of psoriasis?"

I had barely formulated the question in my mind when I heard a bloodcurdling, other-worldly scream.

"Is that your daughter?" I asked, hoping the alarm I felt hadn't crept into my tone. I knew that calm in any emergency was of the essence in dealing with parents and their ill children.

"Yes," he replied, again flatly.

I said, "You need to call an ambulance."

He replied tonelessly, "I am not going to do that. I have been waiting for your office to open. My insurance will not cover an ambulance. I want to bring her in."

I heard another scream.

"You need to call an ambulance *now*!" I declared with authority in my voice.

"No!" he declared, with equal vigor. "Didn't you hear me? My insurance won't pay for it!"

I replied, "I will call my husband and let him talk to you!"

I paged my husband, but he didn't answer his page. I called the hospital and asked them to page him on the intercom, which they did, but there was no reply. No doubt he was driving between hospitals. What should I do?

I remembered that a new dermatologist had arrived in town about a month earlier. I decided to give her a call. Would she even be there? It was now 7:15 a.m. Who would have office hours that early? And if she was in her office, would she take my call?

I was in luck. A receptionist answered the phone. I quickly outlined that I thought one of our patients was in a crisis apparently regarding psoriasis, and that I would appreciate talking to the doctor. The receptionist immediately put the doctor on the line.

The doctor told me, "If psoriasis enters the brain stem, it can be a life or death crisis! I have the authority to call the ambulance. What is their address?"

I quickly gave her the address and called the father to say that an ambulance was on the way.

This child was met at the hospital emergency entrance by two dermatology specialists armed with a morphine drip. She was hospitalized for several days. (By the way, the insurance paid for the ambulance ride.)

I thought to myself, "To hell with the insurance forms!"

I needed some down time. I went into our lounge and made myself a pot of coffee. My husband came in and said, "I'm so glad to see that you are relaxing and not doing clerical work!"

A month or so later this child came into our office for a routine physical. The mother talked to me for a time, never mentioning the incident that was so seared upon my brain. Her main concern was that her daughter was a vegetarian and that she didn't know much about cooking for her.

I left the office, drove home, and looked over my cookbook collection of several hundred books. I selected my most prized vegetarian cookbook, drove back to the office, and presented it to the mother as a gift.

I believe she appreciated the cookbook more than the intervention I had done to get her daughter the service she needed at the time of crisis.

Under pressure, parents do not necessarily react with reasonableness, nor do they necessarily understand what has been done for them. In my Christian tradition Christ said, "Feed my lambs!" I felt that I understood those words for the first time.

ASPHYXIA

A classmate of mine was thinking of going into medical research, and as a lowly intern I was flattered when he asked me to advise him. His wife was pregnant and he wanted her to have the best of care for her delivery. I recommended that they should choose a University-affiliated obstetrician and have the delivery at University Hospital.

Afterwards, he told me about their experience. The baby was born not breathing, and the primitive resuscitative efforts of that day and age were unsuccessful. After thirteen minutes, the obstetrician came out of the delivery room to advise the young father that he should be prepared for the worst. He then re-entered the delivery room, only to burst out again through the doors.

"He's breathing! He started up on his own!"

My classmate was elated, and I congratulated him, but I couldn't help thinking to myself that thirteen minutes of asphyxia would surely result in cerebral palsy.

I took my residency in a distant city and heard only intermittently from my friend. He had gone into medical research and had become the director of a large laboratory. I heard nothing of any handicap of his child.

We met again, by chance, after more than twenty years. I asked about his son.

"Oh, yes," he said. "I'm glad you asked. This year he begins his professorship at the University. He wrote a brilliant thesis, and the University has asked him to stay on."

AUTOPSY

I was not yet a medical student. I was a humble applicant to medical school, demonstrating my commitment by volunteering to work during the summer as a pathologist's assistant. The autopsy room was located deep in the sub-basement of Doctors' Hospital, and my job was to scrub off the shining stainless-steel autopsy table after the pathologist had done his work, using a hose with lots of running water and a lot of plain elbow grease. It had to be made pristine, shining, after each use.

Moments after the orderlies had positioned the cadaver on the table and then disappeared, the pathologist entered through the heavy steel door of the autopsy room. A gray-haired man of medium height and somewhat more than medium bulk, already clad in white gown, surgical gloves, and face mask, he turned immediately to his task. For two or more hours there was silence in the room except for occasional commands for instruments and the pathologist's ritual announcements of measurements, descriptions of excised organs, and pathology, delivered in a loud didactic voice to the hanging microphone attached to the surgical lamp above the table.

The pathologist disappeared and the pathology resident appeared. His task was to supply the pathology technician with the pieces of appendix, gallbladder, and other tissues and organs that had been designated for sectioning and study under the microscope. He had little time for a mere volunteer like myself, but occasionally he allowed himself some small talk. It ran to money.

"Pathology is where the money is," he said. "Pathology and radiology."

I submitted that I was more inclined to clinical practice, or even research. He was dismissive.

"Just wait," he said. "You'll see. You'll go where the money is."

I could already see. I made a mental note to myself to stay away from pathology and radiology.

BACKING INTO THE FAN

It's unusual to have two children from the same family in the hospital at the same time. This family had five, ranging in age from eight years down to the youngest, at six months, all with terrifying coughs. The youngest was seriously ill, with pneumonia and episodes of strangling cough, culminating in the agonized whoop that gave the disease its common name.

There was nothing to set this family apart from a thousand others. They were hard-working but poor, and having heard that some children react badly to immunizations, they had put off indefinitely the expense and anxiety of getting their children immunized.

BIG CLINIC

Solo practice in the badlands of Montana, the only pediatrician for 150 miles in any direction. I realized my life span would be short if I didn't make a change.

The invitation came from a large group practice in Pennsylvania, a sort of "little Mayo Clinic." There would be two of us doing pediatrics. Even time for some research.

It doesn't work out that way. I am being worked to death. I have no control over my appointments. I am booked every fifteen minutes, all day, every day. The hospital portion of the Clinic has, on the average, forty pediatric patients on any given day, many of them extremely, even fatally, ill, and it's my job to attend rounds on all of them twice daily, morning and evening, that is, before and after my scheduled outpatients. Every other night, every other weekend, I am on call all night. That's when most of the patients are admitted. I attend deliveries, stabilize sick newborns, run to the emergency room day or night when called.

After a full day in the outpatient department and a long evening admitting eight or ten sick children I am so exhausted I begin to lose track of their individual histories.

I have repeatedly asked for some help, some relief from this killing pace, with no result. It's under advisement. It's not in the budget. Paying a resident to cover the emergency room would cost ten dollars an hour. They've already got me; why should they do it?

I drive home, eat a cold supper, fall into bed beside my wife. The phone rings. Rising wearily, I dress, get in the car and thread my way through thick fog down the narrow blacktop to the railroad crossing at the base of the bridge.

The gates were down, the warning bell clanged endlessly, and in the darkness I saw the shape of the great locomotive, its headlight catching the drifting fog in its searing single beam.

To get to the Clinic's emergency room I had to cross the bridge over the river; to get to the bridge, I had to cross the railroad tracks. I might wait here for half an hour while a patient's life ebbed away. There would be an inquiry; the emergency room nurse would testify that she had called the doctor at eleven-thirty, that he did not appear until an hour later. Clearly, a dereliction of duty.

I looked for a way around the crossing gates—not promising.

At almost the last moment the great train sighed and began to glide slowly backwards, not far, a few yards only, but enough to trigger the gates, which rose with almost mocking alacrity. Afraid of being trapped between the gates, which could close again as quickly as they had opened, I gunned the car, lurched over the rails and gained the bridge.

On the hospital floor, I hear the elevator doors open behind me. Casters clatter as a bassinet is hastily pushed forward. The babe inside is deeply jaundiced, swollen, bloated—clearly suffering from erythroblastosis fetalis due to Rh-incompatibility.

I groan to myself. This will take four or five hours. The babe will need one, possibly two, exchange transfusions. Fortunately the nurse on duty is young and enthusiastic. She quickly sets in motion the necessary orders, gets the infant ready for exchange.

There is a problem. The blood bank has no blood of the proper type. The transfusion can't proceed without blood.

The nurse steps forward. She has the right type of blood. She'll give a pint of blood.

Half an hour later she returns with the precious gift of life, still warm from her own body.

After that it's pretty routine. I stand under the surgical lamp in the treatment room putting in a few milliliters of blood, then taking out a similar amount, slowly, slowly, repetitively, as the hours tick by. The infant is looking better.

By four in the morning I am ready to go home. Returning the same way I had come, I reach my own home in the half-light of dawn and fall into bed beside my sleeping wife.

Next morning the infant is better. The Head Nurse confronts me angrily. I had allowed a nurse to leave her station for a full half-hour during duty hours.

"But she went to give her own blood to save the baby!"

"No matter. She left her station. She has been formally reprimanded. It will go on her record."

Curse all bureaucrats. Curse all supervisors. Hearts of stone.

CASH IN ADVANCE

Gall-stone attacks are not common in children, but they can occur in young adults. The nurse assigned to work with me in the pediatric clinic was a young mother of two. While at home over the weekend she was suddenly doubled over by excruciating pain in the right upper quadrant of her abdomen. In the emergency room she was diagnosed with gallstone colic.

As the pain abated somewhat, she was sent home with instructions to return on Monday for gallbladder surgery. This she did. She presented herself at the admitting desk on Monday morning. The admitting clerk informed her that she would have to pay cash in advance. Eight hundred dollars. (This was in the 1960's).

"But I am a staff nurse here. Can't you just bill me, or take it out of my pay?"

The answer was no. She went to the bank, drew out her life savings, and paid cash in advance.

DAMAGED BRAINS

The Soviet authorities allowed him to emigrate to America with his adoptive Russian parents because he was a handicapped child, the victim of a postencephalitic syndrome, who needed specialist care not available in Russia. He arrived complete with skull x-rays and medical records, a two-year-old who had spent his entire life in a state institution.

I did a complete exam, looked at the films, and told his new parents that they had a perfectly normal child. He did not have a postencephalitic syndrome.

"But—the records?"

"I don't care what the records say. He's perfectly normal. Take him home and enjoy him."

It took them a while to accept this staggering new finding, but when he began speaking English and playing ball with the other kids, they began to entertain the possibility that he was normal. When he got up to school age and began doing well in school, they were convinced.

I also ignored the records that showed he had been completely immunized. I re-immunized him from scratch.

When the time came for them to move to another city, they gave me a beautiful volume of color plates of the Tsar's Faberge eggs and a big box of Russian chocolates.

I kept the book and threw away the chocolates. In Russia, fantasy is real, and reality is fantasy.

56

DAWN PHYSICALS

Dawn comes early in the Montana badlands, even in early September. The sun was already up at 6AM when the call came from the hospital. There was a patient—no, four patients—waiting for me in the Emergency Room. They were all from one family. They needed school physicals.

"School physicals?" Had I heard right?

"Yes, doctor. They're from the big ranch south of here. It's harvest time. They've been here since 4AM. They waited in their car in the hospital parking lot until six, because they knew you need your sleep."

I did four school physicals that morning, before the school bell rang.

DEMON SEED

"I think this baby is a demon seed. She deliberately tries to hurt me. She fights me at every turn. She won't do anything I want her to do."

The baby on her lap seemed like a normal little four-month-old baby girl to me. Should I have this woman committed to the psych ward? Should I put the child in the hospital to protect her from her mother? But the woman didn't seem crazy to me, and the child didn't look like a demon seed, so I decided to deal with the situation by myself. This was many years ago, when society expected doctors to act on their own without having to look over their shoulder at review boards. Malpractice lawsuits were unheard of. But by the same token, I was stuck with this problem. It was my baby, so to speak.

I said, "If this little girl is a demon seed, then you need to learn some strategies to protect yourself."

To my amazement, Mom heaved a huge sigh of relief and said, "That's exactly what I need!" She enthusiastically agreed to come to my Sunday afternoon parenting class and learn some strategies to protect herself. She went home, left the baby with Daddy (who was the designated babysitter for that day), and went back to her own work.

When she showed up the following Sunday at the parenting class, the first thing she said was that her husband had confronted her that first day when she got home from work and had said, "What on earth did that doctor do to her? She's been a perfect angel all afternoon!"

I was young then and didn't know anything about anything, but I did know enough to smile and keep my mouth shut about things I didn't understand.

That young mother and her husband came to the class faithfully, year after year. As the years went by and they got more and more skilled in the art of human relations, the picture emerged. Their little girl was perfectly normal but she simply would not obey a direct order. The mother discovered this on her own. One day she noticed that little Katy had obeyed her without any objection, and going over it in her mind, she realized she had used the words, "Do you want to do this?" She tried using that exact phrase for several different things, and to her amazement, Katy would automatically answer, "Yes." The obedience problem was solved! The demon seed problem was a matter of using the right words!

I couldn't believe this, so the next time Katy came in for a checkup, I deliberately used the phrase, "Do you want?" for each stage of the exam.

"Do you want to climb up on my table?"

"Yes!" And she did it!

"Do you want to let me look in your ears with my flashlight?"

"Yes!"

I could hardly believe it, but there it was. And because I had videotaping equipment in my office, I made a record of the whole checkup. Mom and Dad gave me permission to use it for teaching purposes because it was a revelation to them, too.[4]

As time went on, Mom and Dad became regulars at the parenting class and we began to learn some interesting things. Mom was raised as an Army brat. That's what she called herself. Her Dad was a high-ranking Army officer and

4 You can view this video at www.higherlevelparenting.com at Section II, Chapter 15, Module Seven, "Refuses direct requests."

he expected instant obedience to every order he gave, even at home. He really believed in Command-and-Control, and his daughter bought into it. Katy's Mom grew up with the unspoken assumption that a family was a little army unit and everybody had to obey orders, but little Katy wasn't having any of it.

How this got transmitted to a four-month old baby I'll never understand, but little Katy, at four months, was in full rebellion and was prepared to fight to the death for her own autonomy. I truly believe this case could have ended in tragedy, were it not for those three little words, "Do you want?" That was when I began to appreciate the real power of human communication for good or for evil.

Katy was five years old when she showed up again in my office. She wanted to talk to me about First Grade. She had started in the Fall even though she was a little young for First Grade. After a few days she told her teacher that she didn't want to attend all day. She explained that she was only a little girl and a half-day was just fine, but a whole day was too long for her. The teacher told her it was the law. She had to go all day.

Katy asked to talk to the principal. She repeated her request to the principal. The principal said it was the law and she had to go all day. Then Katy told her mother what had happened and her mother didn't know what to do. Katy began to lose weight. She cried a lot and sometimes she threw up. She was a very sad little girl. Finally she said, "I want to go and talk to Doctor Gall." Her mother agreed and so they came to me, and Katy told me the whole story.

I replied, "Little girls and boys ought not to have to work all day long, even if it's just First Grade and supposed to be fun. If it's not fun, if it's just tiring, they shouldn't have to do it." I told her Mom and Dad, "If they can't accommodate her request, let her stay in Kindergarten until next year, or whenever she feels old enough."

Katy stayed in Kindergarten. The next year she went to First Grade all day and had a wonderful time.

Katy didn't have School Phobia, even though she had all the symptoms they list in that big book of mental disorders. She simply knew that a full day was just too long for her, and she said so. She kept on appealing to higher authorities until she reached someone who would listen.

How can we teach children what freedom is if we don't listen to them and respect their individual situations?

DICK AND JANE

When my late wife, Beth, and I and our two children moved to Michigan, in the Fall of 1963, our younger son did not take the transition well. He did not welcome changes in his life. I had read the work of Chess and Alexander about the Initial Negative child, but never thought of applying it to my own offspring. That kind of awareness was still thirty years in the future for me.

We lived only half a block from his new elementary school. We thought it was an ideal arrangement. David came home grumbling. He had been provisionally assigned to the slower group of students.

"Mom, they made me a Bluebird! Everybody knows the Bluebirds are the dummies!"

Later, he railed against the reading assignments.

"Dick and Jane! Dick and Jane! Dick and Jane make me vomit!"

Two months later came the Kennedy assassination. All normal life ceased. The TV, shocked for once out of its accustomed banality, carried the story as it unfolded. The two children sat cross-legged on the floor, watching. Beth made sandwiches for meals. She and I hugged each other, cried, stood staring out the window of our tiny apartment.

Four months later, in March, we celebrated David's sixth birthday. Twenty kids from the neighborhood ate cake, wore paper hats, blew raucous noisemakers, popped balloons. David was asked to stand and say a word.

"I'm happier than I'm supposed to be," he said, and sat down.

Beth and I looked at each other, alarmed and uncomprehending. What did fate have in store for our beloved son?

ELEVEN BINKIES

A three-year-old girl came in for her checkup. She was wearing a binkie-necklace—eleven binkies on a string around her neck.

I asked her mother about it.

"She has a binkie for every occasion."

The little girl seemed very happy with that arrangement.

The following year the necklace was gone. I asked her mother about it.

"She had enough. She was ready to move on."

I told this story to another mother who was worried. Her daughter had her binkie in her mouth all the time. It interfered with speaking. The orthodontist was worried about her tooth alignment.

I spoke directly to the little girl.

"Now, about your binkie."

I saw the wariness in her face. Her binkie was firmly in place.

"That's your binkie, and you get to keep it, and use it whenever you like."

Slowly the smile spread over her face, like dawn breaking.

"Mom, I'm really happy!" She began to dance a little jig.

"I'm really, really happy!" She danced in circles around the room.

Mom said to me, "You've really made her day!"

I said, "Have you ever seen one of those people who can't stand the sight of a little child with a binkie in their mouth? They will even cross the street to jerk it out of a child's mouth, even if it's not even their own child."

"Oh, yes!"

"You can just bet that that's what happened to them. Someone took away their binkie when they were little, and they've never gotten over it."[5]

EMERGENCY MOTHER

Her mother died three days after delivery, of a burst aneurysm of the brain. The baby remained in the nursery for ten days, cared for by the nurses. Then a friend of her mother, a young widow, volunteered to help out.

Her father brought the baby to see me on the tenth day. The baby's eyes were ominously dark. She did not smile. She lay quietly in the baby carrier.

Her father asked me what to do.

"You must find another mother for her immediately," I said.

When he brought her back for her six-week checkup, the young widow was with him. I examined the baby, who smiled and seemed normal except for an undefinable overeagerness to please.

The father spoke. "I did what you recommended. My baby has a mother now."

The young widow smiled, and I knew that disaster had been averted.

FIGHT IN THE EXAM ROOM

Carol A. Gall

It was flu season, and the grey sky of the early morning was as dreary looking as my mood. The office was sure to be inundated with sick children. Their mothers often became panicked, lacking the perspective of earlier generations of mothers who had had to deal with mumps, measles, chicken pox, whooping cough, and many other childhood diseases not often seen today. Indeed, often mothers would bring in children barely ill at all, concerned about fevers of 100 degrees. In our office the mothers expected the doctor to wave his magic wand while prescribing an antibiotic, or at least expected him to recommend Tylenol, not realizing that a fever is the body's way of self-treating illness, and if it is not too high, a fever can be greeted with favor rather than fervor.

Today, however, the children who would be seen would most likely be truly ill, and the mothers would need the counsel of my husband to help them through both their fears and the specific medical needs of their children.

My expectations proved accurate. We had the day's schedule full a half hour after arrival.

It was on that day that Jack and Marcy Mansfield arrived without an appointment, Jack carrying their three year old daughter, Alice, in his arms. Jack was dressed in a business suit, as befitted his profession; Marcy wore an attractive pants suit.

Alice had asthma, and this day she was gasping for breath in an alarming fashion.

The Mansfields were used to Alice's breathing problems, but were unaware that this was not her usual asthmatic attack. Alice's face was beginning to have a blue tinge to it. One nurse hurriedly ushered Jack, Marcy, and Alice Mansfield into an examination room, then ran to fetch my husband from another exam room. Another nurse, mumbling that she had not had to administer oxygen for at least ten years said, "I hope I remember how to work the damn tank!" She dislodged it from its usual place in the front office and hauled it to the room where my husband was assessing the situation.

By now the waiting room was full of sick children and there were no places left to sit down. The nurses ushered two of the sickest children and their mothers into vacant rooms. Others were left to stand or to sit on the floor.

It was only a moment after looking at Alice that my husband instructed the nurse to call for an ambulance.

"An ambulance!" Jack declared moodily. "I suppose they'll think they have to take her to the University Hospital! If they do, our insurance won't pay for it. Damned road repair! Well, I'll tell them a thing or two! Over my dead body! They will take her to the hospital that I say she is going to go to."

The mother chimed in, not hiding her derision for her husband in either her voice or her demeanor. Drawing her body straight and puffing out her chest she challenged her husband saying, "Jack, what is the matter with you? Are you a fool? You don't get to dictate where she goes. She needs to go to the hospital that the ambulance can get to the quickest, and right now with all the road work going on, that is the University!"

Jack retorted, his voice rising in volume, "You are an uppity woman! You do not get to say! I get to say!"

Marcy responded in kind. She was shaking with the ferocity of a mother cat hissing at an intruder threatening her kittens. "I am her mother! I do so get to say!"

Neither parent seemed to notice that their little girl had stopped trying to breathe in the oxygen. My husband had a momentary tinge of fear in his eyes. He said to the mother using his slow, soft, hypnotic speech, "Would you please help me with this? I want you to get the blanket inside that cabinet over there." He pointed at a steel cabinet across the room that held supplies. "Why don't you cover her up a little? I think she is getting a bit cold."

I recognized this as a distraction technique designed to get the parents to stop fighting. Their angry words were not helping their child to relax and breathe.

By now the grey sky was releasing its moisture with a vengeance. I knew if the ambulance had any chance of getting close to our medical building, that someone would have to go out and prevent people from double parking next to the entrance. I supposed that someone would have to be me.

I went outside and stood in the downpour, cold rain hitting my face, which was probably just as well. It was a distraction from the tension of the unfolding drama inside.

Sure enough, for fifteen minutes I had to shoo away car after car. Most drivers just looked resignedly at me, but one man shook his fist at me angrily, and I felt vindicated when just as he pulled into one of the few remaining spaces at the back of the lot, the ambulance, red lights flashing, sirens blaring, arrived.

The paramedics wanted me to brief them on what was happening, as they got their gear out of the back of the ambulance.

I said, "I am not the doctor, I am the doctor's wife!"

One of the paramedics said grumpily, "Well, you were in there, weren't you? What did the Doc say?"

(In a crisis, I had learned, niceties are often brushed aside; in fact, niceties may seem like luxuries. Thus I was not especially surprised that the paramedic barked at me, though I can't say I ever really got used to that sort of attitude. Now it was my turn to silently bark at another. The man who had shook his fist at me had to walk right past me to get to the entrance to keep whatever appointment he had in the building.

He looked quite embarrassed as his gaze met mine. I glared at him anyway.)

I returned my attention to the paramedics. I said, "The doctor says this three-year-old girl is going to need transport. Her oxygen saturation level is quite low. Her parents were fighting over what hospital she was going to go to when I came outside. The little girl was unable to relax enough to try to breathe in the oxygen they were trying to administer to her. That was fifteen minutes ago, when we called you."

They wheeled in the gurney and I directed them to the correct exam room and stood just outside the open door. The father immediately began again his tirade about where the ambulance would go. The biggest, burliest man among the paramedics turned to the father and said, "The ambulance goes where *I* decide it goes!" He had the authority that a low voice and bulk combined with the truth can give; the father acquiesced.

It seemed like an eternity before the paramedics left with little Alice. My husband calmly called the next person into an exam room and went on seeing patients. I asked him briefly in the hallway how he could manage to stay so calm in so dire a situation. He said, "I can't do my work if I allow myself to have an emotional response. I have a responsibility to my patients."

I, on the other hand, went into our bathroom and threw up.

That night at dinner when I was bemoaning the behavior of Alice's parents and castigating them soundly, my husband said, "It's not uncommon for parents to do things like that. It's merely tension releasing itself. Not all people have self-control in these matters. You can't assume you are seeing people as they usually behave."

Six years into retirement John accompanied me to my appointment to see an orthopedic surgeon, Dr. Frank Wales, about some tenosynovitis in my left hand, which had rendered me unable to play the piano. He explained to me that the synovial fluid was unable to lubricate the tendon, which usually slid back and forth inside the sheath like a piston in a car engine. The surgeon gave me a steroid shot at the base of the middle finger, left hand, in an attempt to cause the sheath to return to its normal size.

When he was finished the doctor said to us, "You might enjoy reading "Hot Lights, Cold Steel" by Dr. Michael J. Collins. He and I were at the Mayo Clinic at the same time and Dr. Collins was selected to be the Chief Resident of Orthopedics."

My husband, as well, had been a Chief Resident in his field, Pediatrics, and we both thought it would be an interesting book to read. Perhaps some of their experiences would parallel one another. When we got home, I went on-line and ordered the book. A few days later it arrived.

In lieu of television or other entertainment, John and I often read to one another in the evenings. We decided to read this book together. It was my turn to read, so I opened the book and began to read aloud the prelude to the book, the sad and moving story of young Kenny Johannson. Kenny had been run over by a tractor and was badly injured. Dr. Collins was faced with the decision of whether or not to try to save his leg; saving it could cost Kenny his life. The kid was just fourteen years old.

As I was reading aloud Dr. Collin's description of the agonizing decision he faced, I glanced over at my husband. Tears were streaming silently down his cheeks.

"Is this too much for you?" I asked, both surprised and concerned over my husband's tears.

He said, "The entire fifty years I was in practice I held back my emotions so that I could think clearly in these kinds of situations."

I thought to myself, "Fifty years of tears are coming out now."

I thought of his work in solo practice in Montana, where he was greeted, along with the moving van, with a scrawled note posted on the front door instructing him to report urgently to the local hospital, where a newborn baby needed a blood transfusion.

I thought of his work at the Clinic in Pennsylvania where he cared for thirty or forty critically ill babies every day for three years.

I thought of his patients in Michigan, remembering the day he had gotten lab tests back on a child who most certainly had sickle cell anemia. He couldn't locate the mother and her daughter who were shopping, as it turned out, at the mall. The teen-ager needed an immediate blood transfusion.

So many children, so many parents, so many crises . . .

John cried softly for a time, and I put the book away, grateful for the trigger for the release of those closely held emotions. We would read the book another day.

FIREMAN SAM

Matthew's parents were well-educated and idealistic and understood that children are to be treated with respect. They knew there was such a thing as Sibling Rivalry and they looked for signs of it when the new baby came, but Matthew seemed to accept the new baby, even to love him. He even behaved himself when Mom nursed the new arrival.

What puzzled them was Matthew's strange new obsession, a game he played every morning after breakfast. In that game, the playhouse in the nursery was on fire. Matthew had a new name. He was Fireman Sam. He insisted that his mother call him Fireman Sam. He came running into the nursery with his big toy fire engine, unrolled the fire hose and sprayed the imaginary fire with imaginary water. Mom had to participate as Nurse Jane, to help get the people out of the burning building.

Matthew's parents came to me to ask what it all meant, and what should they do. I told them I had no idea, but I thought it would be useful for Mom to cooperate fully for as long as necessary. "Fireman Sam" continued to appear every morning for over six months, then gradually faded away.

Both boys are now in college, doing well.

FIRST PATIENT

The big change comes in the second term of the second year, when the clinical clerkships begin.

Each of us had bought our own little black bag containing stethoscope and otoscope and other diagnostic instruments, the little tuning forks and the tape measures and all the mysterious magic paraphernalia, the possession of which somehow converted us in our own minds into real physicians.

Now we were permitted to wear the short white coat of the clinical clerk and—Oh wonder! Oh thrill!—to walk onto the wards and actually examine people, flesh to flesh. We were to lay hands on the sick. This more than any other was the magic moment, the turning point at which the green medical student makes the transition into fledgling doctor.

That first patient was the moment of truth.

I found myself that January morning standing on the tar-stained concrete in front of the crumbling concrete entrance to the old Gallinger Hospital. I didn't even know enough to find the way to my assigned ward and had to wander here and there, looking for elevators, begging directions off of orderlies and janitors and finally emerging through a half-dozen strange wards to find one where I seemed to be expected.

I was given the name of my patient. I stepped into the ward. On each side the peeling white-enameled beds were ranged in two neat rows, probably fifty or sixty beds in all, and all occupied.

Some had the white curtains drawn already as the students who had arrived earlier toiled over their histories and physical exams. I walked down the aisle, looking for the names taped to the foot of the bed, and keenly aware that every occupant was staring at me, not curiously, but indifferently as people do who have nothing to do and will follow any diversion even the wandering flight of a fly, but to me in my present state of mind it seemed they were all looking at me mockingly, wondering if I had sense enough to find the right patient or whether I would be one of those occasional ones who lose their nerve, turn abruptly around and walk rapidly out of the ward and never return. The thought actually entered my head but I kept on grimly, face red, ears burning, until I found my man. Thank God I hadn't drawn the female ward.

Timidly I introduced myself to the grizzled, white-haired old man in the bed, then pulled the white curtains for privacy, getting a little tangled in the process but not fatally for my self-command.

Then I sat down in the visitor's chair beside the bed and pulled out my notebook and the little forbidden outline of points to cover in the history and physical exam. I was determined not to leave anything out. I would write it all down.

The old man was only too happy to comply. His whole life history spilled out of him, seventy years of it, chapter and verse in detail so sure and precise that he must have rehearsed it a million times mentally. Maybe it was all the old man ever had to do any more, just rehearse his life history.

Time passed and my hastening pen raced on, one hour, then two, the mounting restlessness turning to malaise, then outright anxiety, and finally panic. This old man was not going to stop, ever. I was trapped there in a frozen eternity with seventy years being spun out in the little white-sheeted cubicle like a winding sheet for me. I was becoming mummified as the old man wrapped me in layer after layer of private experiences.

Lunch time was long past, I had missed the one o'clock class, and I hadn't even gotten to the physical examination. In desperation I stood up suddenly, interrupting the old man in full cry.

"I must examine you now," I said, but even as I said it I saw the flicker of amusement in the his eyes; and before I had even instructed him what to do the old man had sat up straight in bed, swinging his short hairy legs (even there his hair was white) over the bedside and pulled open the white gown that tied behind, around the neck and the waist, dropping it from his shoulders so that it fell to the waist.

With a bony finger that shook no more than it should for a man of that age he pointed to a spot below the left nipple and another at the base of the neck, near the breastbone. Both spots were clearly marked with little crosses in blue ink, so that he looked like one of the diagrams in the Physical Diagnosis textbook. He leaned forward and whispered confidentially.

"The other medical students listened right there and there. You listen there and you'll hear it, too. It's an aneurysm of the ascending aorta, doctor; a big one. I've had it for years. You know what it comes from, I don't need to tell a smart boy like you. I don't mind admitting how I got it, either. Yes, I was a devotee of Venus in my youth, doctor, and this is the end result. But thank goodness, my head is all right. It never affected my mind. And I'm not sorry for anything."

He cackled in glee.

There was no possible way out. I had to stand there and go through with it. Ears burning, face scarlet, I placed my stethoscope at the indicated points and listened to what I now knew in advance I was going to hear, the swish-swish of a big aneurysm, the blood boiling around in that sack the size of a small kettle. But just to redeem a little bit of the situation I ostentatiously listened at other places too, palpating the posterior chest wall and finishing up with a careful examination of the pupillary reflexes and the eyegrounds that was really longer than necessary, considering what I had already been told.

Then I gathered up the instruments, which had gotten scattered all over the bed amongst the worn and torn but still white sheets and the folds of the old man's gown, stuffed them awkwardly into the little black bag, said my goodbye, and fled.

"Come back and see me again," the old man hooted after me. "You will be a good doctor—you listen to what the patient says!"

HE'S ALREADY BEEN GOOD TO ME

She was a sixteen-year-old single mother, delivered during the night of a baby boy. She was assigned to me because she hadn't selected a pediatrician. I introduced myself and congratulated her. Before I could say another word, she announced proudly,

"He's already been good to me!"

After the visit, I called my late wife Beth. "There's trouble coming with this one," I said. "She's going to need all the help she can get."

"HE'S SUCH A BOY!"[6]

Pediatricians have long recognized that the basic processes that work to form a new person are very robust, and that most of our efforts are aimed at helping those processes to work undisturbed. Supply vitamin D, and the child will grow his own straight bones. Supply a rich and nurturing social environment, and the child will develop his own personality. There is mystery and magic in those processes by which an infant builds, out of raw, unformed matrices, the structures that become the differentiated adult.

Gender identity is one of those mysterious processes. You can see it taking form even in the first few months after birth. Girl babies one month old flirt with their Dads and are all business around Mom. A year later they like Mom better. It's an extremely robust process, and the average parent will never have to give it a second thought.

When parents do bring up the issue, it is usually to report, wonderingly, that their fifteen-month-old boy insists on banging toys together and shoving wheeled toys around to the sound of motor-like noises. As one Mom, single by choice, told me, "I used to be an environmental person—you know, a believer that the environment controlled this. But he's *such a boy*, and nobody taught him!"

One little boy, just 27 months old, came to my office with his football—almost as big as he was—and spent the whole time throwing it up and catching it, dropping it, running after it, and repeating the whole sequence.

Dads sometimes worry when their toddler son insists on carrying around a stuffed toy. I reassure them that the stuffed toy is not a doll. It is a surrogate identity figure and must be respected at all costs.

---

6 First published in the Senior Bulletin of the American Academy of Pediatrics, Fall, 2007, under the title "The Mysterious Processes of a New Person." This interview can be viewed online at www.higherlevelparenting.com, Section One, Chapter Five, Module Eight.

Girls have surrogate identity figures too. At sixteen months:

Mom: Well, she rubs its nose. She had a lot of cold, and she apparently gets a tissue and she will rub the little baby's nose.

Doctor: "The doll has a runny nose because I have a runny nose," so to speak.

A three-year-old girl complains about the new baby: "He crawls in my room and knocks over my dollies." I sympathize and make alliance with her and her mother to "keep that kid out of your room."

Shyness is not a gender identity issue. Both boys and girls have a right to use shyness to protect their boundaries and control interactions with others until they feel secure enough to drop that defense.

Gender identity is a process that you watch unfold. You are not in charge of it. Attempts at deliberate, conscious control are not likely to have any success at all. It almost always turns out the way you hope and expect. What you can do is to avoid messing in and messing up that process.

HONORING FATHER

He was sixteen years old when his father, a distinguished physician, died in a freak auto accident. A few months later, he and his mother appeared in my office. It was time for his annual physical.

"He's going to Europe this summer in a youth-exchange program. He has volunteered to participate in a sky-diving exhibition."

I spoke to him directly.

"Your father died too young. I know you loved him very much, but he would not want you to die even though you loved him very much. Go to Europe, but don't do the parachuting. You don't need to die to show him how much you loved him."

HOW NOT TO EXAMINE A BABY

Recently I watched a very competent professor of pediatrics as he examined a newborn baby.

The baby was waving his arms and legs, opening and closing his mouth, blinking and looking around, and spontaneously exhibiting that marvelous range and repertoire of behavior that newborn babies have.

The doctor began his examination.

He tried to look in the baby's mouth by pulling the baby's jaw open. Reflexly, the baby clamped his jaw shut and the doctor had to pry it open with a tongue blade.

The doctor tried to examine the baby's hands and pulled his fingers out into extension. Reflexly, the baby clenched his fists and the doctor had to pry them open.

The doctor wanted to look in the baby's ear with his instrument, and the baby reflexly swept his arm over that ear, so that the doctor had to have help in holding the baby's hand away from the ear.

He tried to measure the baby's head with a tape measure and the baby began to turn his head from side to side to be rid of the tight band around his head.

He shone his light in the baby's eyes and the baby screwed his eyelids shut.

This went on and on. The doctor was doing exactly what he had been taught in medical school—how to examine a baby from head to toe, by the numbers. The baby had already spontaneously done all the things that the doctor wanted, but that was before the doctor had officially started, and when the doctor tried to do the examination in the officially approved sequence, he himself unknowingly and unconsciously elicited the very opposite of each particular behavior that he wanted at that particular moment.

By demanding jaw opening, he got jaw closing.

By demanding fist opening, he got fist closing.

By demanding eye opening, he got eye closing. And so on.

His attempt to call forth behavior from the system called "baby" resulted in the opposite behavior from what he wanted.

And he didn't notice!

Now the doctor had certainly paid attention to his own professors in medical school. He had certainly paid attention when he was watching his professors do their examinations. He was certainly doing what he had been taught to do, and he was doing what he had seen his professors doing. What he was failing to do was to take note of the feedback he was getting at that very moment from the baby.

Noticing the connection between what you are doing and what happens as a result (feedback) is technically called "contingency detection." Every baby does contingency detection. It's we adults who have lost that ability.

There is a way to touch the back of a baby's hand so that he will spontaneously open it. The baby's eyes will spontaneously open if you turn off the overhead lights. And every mother knows there is a way to get the baby to open his mouth spontaneously.[7] And so on, right down the list.

What that doctor was doing is called pushing on the system (in this case, the baby) to make it work. And that usually gets the opposite result from the one desired, because the system protects itself against the push. It pushes back. This is the problem with good advice of all kinds, all these exhortations to live a healthy life, to not smoke, and so on. They usually just amount to pushing on the system. They generate the very

---

7 You can view an example online at www.higherlevelparenting.com, Section III, Chapter 31, Module 3, "Sock-smell."

resistance that eventually defeats them.

This doctor, who was having so much trouble examining a newborn baby, was not aware that he was having any particular trouble. This situation didn't seem strange to him. He took it for granted that examining a newborn baby involves a kind of fight or wrestling match. That was his unconscious, unexamined metaphor, and he routinely called for a nurse to come and help him hold the baby down. Even the baby knew there was a problem--he cried and called for help. But not the doctor! If you're not aware that you've got a problem, how can you call for help?

I am absolutely sure that this doctor practiced contingency detection when he himself was a baby, but thirty years of higher education had cured him of that. He had lost the power of making the connection between one event and another, of noticing that Y always follows X, and thus he had lost the power of adapting his behavior to the obvious needs of the situation.

A baby who is being examined with proper respect for his feedback doesn't have to be held down to be examined, because he's comfortable. He smiles when you touch the back of his tongue with the tongue blade and trigger off his gag reflex.[8] He thinks that's amusing, and he lets you do it again and again just to experience the curious pleasure of feeling his gag reflex working over and over. And she doesn't regard the ophthalmoscope light as scary or painful, she stares right back at it and smiles. She's having fun. And the otoscope speculum tickling the auditory canal: that's nothing terrible, it's just a very interesting tickling feeling in the ear.

---

8 You can view an example online at www.higherlevelparenting.com, Section III, Chapter 13, Module 1, "Fun."

HOW TO CLIMB A TREE[9]

In the 1960's our older son Duane was in the Webelos, which I understand is something between Cub Scouts and full-fledged Boy Scouts. One Saturday morning my late wife Beth was washing dishes in the kitchen. Our little apartment was on the side of a hill, so the kitchen window was about twenty feet up in the air. Beth looked out the window at the little tree growing in front of the house, and she looked right into Duane's face. He was twenty feet up in that tree.

Beth realized in a flash that if she registered alarm and said, "Don't fall!" that would probably be just enough to cause him to slip and fall.

With great effort she composed herself and smiled and said, "Oh, hi, Duane! I see you are doing your merit badges. And do you know how to climb down again too?"

Duane smiled and said, "Sure. I'll show you!" and he climbed right down.

---

9 Original story in *Elegant Parenting*, 1994.

HOW TO LIVE TO BE A HUNDRED[10]

One of the more futile things in this world is trying to give good advice to teenagers.

With kids approaching the age of sixteen, I sometimes begin the annual checkup by telling them we no longer think in terms of a lifespan of seventy-some years. More and more people are living into their eighties, nineties, even a hundred or more. Some people are living a hundred and ten or even a hundred and twenty years.

I say to them, "Now you may think, 'What's that got to do with me, I'm not even sixteen,' but if you want to live a really long life, you have to avoid getting knocked off before your time. You have to know, the thing that will kill you when you're sixteen, seventeen, all the way up to twenty-six, is the automobile.

"From sixteen to twenty-six, the thing that will kill you is the automobile. So when you get that driver's license at sixteen, you make sure you are the one in that driver's seat. Nobody else gets to drive you unless they are as old as your parents. Because you know your parents know how to drive and you know that you know how to drive, but you don't know how good a driver that other kid is. You know you care about staying alive, but you don't know about the other kid.

"This means, of course, that you're going to have to have your own car!"

"Now, from twenty-six to sixty, the thing that will kill you is cigarettes. Lung cancer. You smoke, you will die before you're sixty. And it's really hard to stop, so don't start.

"Now, after sixty, from sixty on to eighty, ninety, a hundred and ten, that's the tricky part. If you want to live a long and happy life, you have to stay on good terms with your Mom and Dad. You're stuck with them, so you may as well start

10 From *Dancing With Elves*, 2000.

practicing now."

I'm not handing them a set of rules. They've heard so many rules they're sick of rules. I'm just telling them how to live a hundred and ten years.

HOW TO MEET GIRLS

Our older son Duane had already successfully made the transition to University life. He was living in his own apartment on campus and doing well in his studies. My late wife, Beth, and I were proud of him. Then, on a visit, he stumped us both.

"Mom, Dad, how do you meet girls?"

At this point I had been a pediatrician for more than twenty years, but I still didn't know what to say. Beth, a public health nurse, was quicker than I.

"Do something different," she said.

Duane turned to me.

I managed to blurt out, "You need to go where they are," I said.

We didn't see him again for about three weeks.

"I've got a girl friend!" he announced. "I did what you said."

We had forgotten what we had said.

"You said to go where they are, and to do something different. So I got a job as busboy in the local sorority."

It took us a minute to realize he had followed both our instructions.

"It worked! I met the senior who was in charge of dishwashing operations."

"But how—what—?" we asked.

"Oh, it was easy," he said. "She was breaking up with her boyfriend, and I just listened sympathetically, and pretty soon she asked if I would be her new boyfriend."

They went away to separate law schools and got married the week after graduation. And that's how we got our lovely granddaughter.

HOW TO PROP BOTTLES PROPERLY

There is a right and a wrong way to do everything, a right time and place, and a wrong time and place.

At sixteen months, little Philip woke up almost every night for a drink. Sometimes he wanted water, sometimes juice. Mom and Dad were getting tired of being waked up at night, so Dad fashioned a little wooden rack to fit by the side of the crib, big enough to hold three baby bottles. When Philip woke up, he had his choice of water, apple juice, or orange juice. He helped himself, then went back to sleep.

This arrangement worked so well that Mom decided to keep three bottles in the refrigerator at all times. When Philip got thirsty, he went to the refrigerator, opened the door, and picked out the drink he preferred.

Why shouldn't a sixteen-monther, who knows very well what he wants, have a few choices in life?

HYPERACTIVE

"She walks around muttering to herself. She gets up at night and paces around her room, and she's only five years old. We're worried she might be hyperactive."

What else?

"She insists we take her out for entertainment every other night."

What kind of entertainment?

"Plays. Plays with live actors. *Shakespeare!*"

On a hunch, I suggested the parents listen in on the girl after she went to bed at night. They reported back. "She gets up and walks around and recites all the lines of the different actors."

They were advised to drop the hyperactivity idea and get the girl a drama coach.

ISLAMIC CHILD

In some Islamic cultures, if a baby dies or even becomes significantly ill, the mother is held to blame. As a result, many Islamic mothers live in a state of terror for the well-being of their child. They don't dare to be firm. The child picks up both the fear and the lack of firmness.

Yasmin was such a mother, and her little boy played it for all it was worth. Although Yasmin was a tenured University professor, author of definitive texts in her field, she was ruthlessly bossed by her little boy. Yasmin's husband, himself a distinguished literary figure, was equally at a loss. He couldn't understand how a big almost-four-year-old boy still insisted on drinking from a bottle, followed his mother around when she was at home, pooped in his pants and then demanded to be cleaned up.

Yasmin listened with great respect when I gave her advice about how to deal with her son. She was extremely respectful and deferential to me and to all the males in her family, and her son continued to dominate her.

I was flattered by her respect and by her deferential manner. I failed to realize what the problem was, and I too was rewarded with failure.

IT'S A GIFT[11]

When I was a little kid, I used to admire my mother's ability to find four leaf clovers. We would walk together over the front lawn, talking and enjoying the spring weather, and suddenly she would swoop down and pick up a four leaf clover.

"There's one!" she would say and hold it out for me to see. Sure enough, it always had four leaves, not three. "How do you do that?" I would ask. "What's your secret?" And she would say, "You just have to keep your eye out for them."

Well, I tried and tried every way I knew to keep my eye out for four leaf clovers, but every thing I picked up had three leaves. I even got down on my hands and knees and worked my way systematically across the lawn, but it didn't work. Finding four leaf clovers is a gift. My mother had it, I didn't.

A few years ago my wife Carol had as one of her piano students a young Native American boy who was in the third grade and still couldn't read a word. He spoke fluent English as well as his native Ojibway. He had no trouble reading piano music on the page, a more complex task than reading text. In fact, one of his favorite tricks was to play the entire piece backwards, back to front, starting with the last note on the last page. Carol herself (a concert pianist) couldn't do that. In his tribe, he was considered to have such maturity of judgment that he was viewed as a possible future Chief.

Carol didn't think he couldn't read. She thought he *thought* he couldn't read. She thought his *teachers* thought he couldn't read. So she got out her old visual-perceptual testing equipment and put Raymond through his paces. Raymond didn't know this had anything to do with reading. He found the hidden pictures on every page. It was just like seeing the eagle perched on the tree branch in the forest. He didn't know

11 First presented at Graduation Ceremony, Summers-Knoll School, Ann Arbor, Michigan, 2001.

he had aced the test, and that his visual-perceptual skills were at the level of a gifted adult.

Carol got out her old flash cards and taught him to read. In a few weeks he went from being a non-reader to being a reader.

I had a lot of growing up to do before I understood that the word "gifted" always pertains to some cultural context. The Eskimo child who can sense the presence of a seal under the ice would not necessarily be called gifted in New York or London. And when my mother was a schoolgirl in rural Virginia in the early 1900's, her ability to find four leaf clovers was not considered a gift worth noticing. It certainly didn't contribute to her grade-point average. But she taught her children to seek out the hidden truths that lie in plain sight.

KEEP OUT!

Dad was a fussy person who kept monitoring his little boy. Little Nathan, at two years old, was bright enough to defend himself. After the third reminder to stop talking and singing and go to sleep, Nathan would look up at his father and, smiling sweetly, would say,

"Yes, ma'am!"

Dad complained to me,

"He knows just how to get my goat!"

I told Nathan what to say to his Dad the next time his Dad barged in to tell him to go to sleep, and he promised to say it.

"Get the hell out of my room so I can get some sleep!"

It worked, and Nathan slept the sweet sleep of one who has had the last word.

LAUGH IT OFF

I was still a young pediatric resident when I met Eric.

My wife's sister had a married friend who, after several miscarriages, decided to adopt a child.

The agency delivered to them a healthy four-month-old boy who had been in three foster homes. He had been removed from the latest foster home because the foster parents had turned out to be abusive.

My wife and I visited the happy young couple a few days after they had received their final adoption papers. The young adoptive mother placed Eric on my lap. Eric had light blue eyes and a laughing face.

He laughed out loud when I bounced him on my knee, then suddenly launched himself full tilt into my face. His forehead struck my chin with such force that I recoiled and my glasses fell off. Eric, still on my lap, peered into my face and laughed out loud. I put him down to retrieve my glasses and Eric, laughing, crawled away.

Several years later we began to get reports from our young friends. Eric was expelled from successive day-care centers. He would attack other children, knock them down, and run away laughing. Kindergarten, first grade—same problem. An endless series of consultations with psychologists, social workers, and psychiatrists ensued. Medications were prescribed, dosages increased. As Eric grew big and strong and handsome, his escapades grew too. He set fires, stole whatever caught his fancy, fought with playmates.

His adoptive parents, deeply religious and conscientious, sought advice from clergy and child development specialists. They refused to give up hope for their child.

Eric began dealing drugs. When he couldn't pay, strangers appeared demanding money, which his parents paid. The sums demanded grew larger, impossible to pay. Cars drove by in the night. There was gunfire. Eric was beaten up so severely that he was hospitalized, not once, not twice, but repeatedly. He didn't care. He just laughed it off.

A companion was found dead by the highway. Eric was the last person to see him. They had been drinking together. He was sent to jail, then released. He stole a motorcycle, skidded off the road, ended up in the hospital with multiple severe injuries.

Shortly after his release from hospital, he announced he had found and married a girl friend. She was pregnant. Their child was born prematurely. Eric's parents supported the three of them, hoping Eric was at last ready to settle down.

Eric split up with his girl friend. Divorce followed. Eric's parents took in the young mother and their grandchild. Eric decided to go to cooking school, quit cooking school to become cook on a Mississippi river boat. He disappeared, then reappeared, each time with ever more fantastic misadventures, escapades, injuries. Now forty years old, he began a course of body-building to rehabilitate his shattered frame. His parents paid for expensive dental care for his drug-rotted teeth.

Finally, Eric's parents had had enough. They found a half-way house for him and moved him in. Eric stayed in the halfway house a few months, then disappeared. When he reappeared, his parents told him to get lost and stay lost.

The story isn't over yet. Eric is still alive, and his parents know approximately where he is. Having lost their life savings and their hope of a secure if modest retirement, they are still supporting Eric's ex-wife and their grandchild, who is approaching college age. Everyone is awaiting the next series of exploits with fascinated dread.

LIVER-GROWN

"Make the door to."

"The red pills are all, but the blue pills are yet."

It took some getting used to, the language of the Amish. Stolid, sturdy believers, they tilled their lands in the old ways and kept to their beliefs with true Mennonite zeal. They brought in their sick children only when all else failed.

The child lying on the examining table was a fat nine-monther with a length of greasy string tied around his belly.

"I want you to check his belly. I think he's liver-grown."

Suppressing my initial reaction, I asked, "What is this string around his belly?"

"Goose-grease. Against liver-grown."

I couldn't help myself. I had to ask, "What's liver-grown?"

Indignantly she gathered up her baby in her arms.

"I don't want a doctor who doesn't even know what liver-grown is!"

And she marched out.

I never learned what liver-grown is.

LOBOTOMY DOCTOR

I have been lucky in life in that I have mostly been able to avoid close contact with the high and mighty of this world. However, I could not avoid Professor Walter Freeman.

As part of my internship training, I was present along with four or five of my classmates one morning in the penthouse suite of Sibley Hospital, in downtown Washington, D.C. We had been chosen to be observers while Professor Walter Freeman, founder and first President of the newly-established American Board of Neurology and Psychiatry, demonstrated his special skill, the operation for which he was famous and which the good professor was sure would constitute his claim to lasting fame in the annals of neurology, psychiatry, and surgery.

The little penthouse suite was circular, deeply carpeted, totally unlike a surgical operating room. In the middle of the room was a single white pedestal, looking absurdly like a misplaced bird-bath. Two white-coated attendants brought out the patient lying on a gurney, a rather dazed-appearing woman in street clothes. Professor Freeman, shirtsleeves rolled up to reveal his hairy arms, called for anesthesia. The white-coated anesthetist stepped forward, clapped two electrodes to the patient's temples, and fired the electrical charge once, twice, three times. The patient lurched convulsively three times, then subsided, immobile.

Professor Freeman gestured for his operating tools.

An attendant emerged from a side door, bearing a dark red velvet pillow on which rested two large chrome-plated nails—for want of a better word—each about the length of an ice pick and bearing centimeter markings on the shaft, and a chrome-plated mallet with a steel handle. The attendant placed the velvet pillow with the instruments on it on the birdbath. Professor Freeman picked up one nail and the mallet in his bare hands and made a gesture of dismissal. The attendant, looking for all the world like a page in a royal court, retired through the side door.

"As you can see, electrical anesthesia is entirely adequate for this procedure. Furthermore, it is not necessary to provide a sterile field because the conjunctival membranes are naturally sterile, and since the pressure gradient from the eye socket to the brain is uphill, so to speak, any potential contamination would have to travel against that gradient to get into the brain. To put it briefly, you don't have to worry about any of that germ crap. Transorbital lobotomy is ideally adapted to outpatient and even in-home emergency situations. Every doctor should carry a lobotomy instrument and hammer in his medical bag."

The good doctor then stepped forward, pulled the patient's left eyelid up with his thumb, inserted the spike deep into the eye-sac, and with a few quick taps of the chrome-plated hammer drove the spike through the bone at the back of the eye-socket and into the brain. He then tapped the spike further in, to a depth of seven centimeters; then, explaining which tracts needed to be severed, he suddenly rotated the spike through a full three-quarter circle, causing the blunt end to describe an arc in the air in front of the patient's face about four to six inches in diameter. He then quickly picked up the other spike, inserted it in the other eye, and repeated the procedure.

There was a thud behind him as a medical student slumped to the floor.

Professor Freeman grabbed a spike with each hand and pulled them out simultaneously, with a flourish.

"That's it, gentlemen. When she wakes up she'll be better than new."

Better than new? The patient's eyes were ringed with black.

"Those black eyes are beauts, aren't they? Put some dark glasses on her and don't bother to explain. They'll go away."

Professor Freeman went around the country like a politician stumping his constituency, touting the procedure he called transorbital lobotomy and doing hundreds of demonstration operations on the flimsiest of indications, driving the cruel spike through the eye socket and into the brain of fellow human beings whose only offense was to think, feel, and behave in ways that people like Freeman chose to regard as signs of disease. Professor Freeman really knew how to drive a nail.

LOOSE FINGERNAILS

Lucinda's mother was going through a painful divorce. Dad lived far away and never visited, and now Lucinda, just twelve years old, and her Mom were going to have to sell their home and move.

In the midst of all this, Lucinda began to lose her fingernails, first one, then two, then three at a time. They became loose at the far end, at the near end, in the middle, and just plain fell off. I referred them to a dermatologist, who confirmed that once in a great while, usually under stressful conditions, a person's nails can just fall off, and that they would eventually grow in again.

They both were greatly relieved to know that it was not some dreadful disease. They were so relieved about it that Lucinda's nails actually began to grow in again.

LOW-FLYING GOOSE

Four fifty-five on a Friday afternoon is the witching hour in pediatric offices. It's the moment when the most outrageous calls come in. This particular Friday was no exception. The phone rang and the receptionist answered. It was a frantic mom:

"Help! Help! My child has just been struck by a low-flying goose!"

After the initial shock, the receptionist collapsed in spasms of laughter. She couldn't speak into the phone.

My wife picked up the call, asked for details. The caller's son, with two other school kids, had ventured into a thicket of sumac and small trees just off the school property. Within the thicket was a small pond where some Canada geese were resting on the shore. Startled, the geese burst into flight, but in the cramped space of the thicket they were unable to gain altitude in time. One goose collided with the boy, knocking him down and scratching his forehead.

We put a Band-aid on the wound.

MALE ANOREXIA

When President Kennedy was assassinated, our two children were five and seven years old. It was their first direct encounter with death. They sat in front of the TV, quietly watching, and we parents wondered what would come of it.

It wasn't until six months later that we realized that Duane, now eight years old, had lost his baby fat. No, it was more than that. We realized with a pang that his little chin had become razor-sharp. He was slowly but surely losing weight.

My late wife, Beth, and I looked at each other. Terrible possibilities raced through our minds. I ordered laboratory studies. They came back negative.

Beth sat him down and patiently began to question him about his life. He had been giving away his lunch at school, to others "who needed it more than he did."

We praised him for his loving-kindness, but made it clear that this could not go on. He could not give up his own life, one lunch at a time, even for others who needed help.

He stopped giving up his lunches, but his appetite had become down-regulated. It was more than a year until he was eating hearty meals again, and his parents could breathe freely again.

Death is contagious. When one person dies, we all die a little.

As the poet wrote, "No man is an island, entire of itself; every man is a piece of the continent, a part of the main; if a clod be washed away by the sea, Europe is the less, as well as if a promontory were, as well as if a manor of thy friends or of thine own were; any man's death diminishes me, because I am involved in mankind; and therefore never send to know for whom the bell tolls; it tolls for thee."[12]

---

12 John Donne, Devotions XVII.

MAX

In a man's world, Maxine was a star. Small, athletic, with short auburn hair and a commanding nose, she easily held her own among the macho male surgical residents. As I was one of those undecided interns who had chosen to rotate through all the specialties, our paths seldom crossed.

I was just coming out of a patient's room when I saw her sail by at high speed. Strange sounds were coming from the next room. I had just identified them as choking sounds when I saw her dart into the room, pull out a plugged tracheotomy tube, and begin suctioning the man's airway.

The man, a big African-American, was rolling his eyes in extreme distress. As Max continued her suctioning, he began to breathe more quietly. I saw that his entire jaw had been surgically removed. Maxine took a towel and wiped the man's sweating face. He tried to express his gratitude, but there was only a hole where his mouth had been.

Maxine leaned over and kissed him full on the cheek. His eyes filled with tears, and so did mine. When I looked again, Maxine was gone.

MOB REVENGE

The old Gallinger Hospital in Washington, D.C., admitted those who had nowhere else to go. My patient, that night, burst from the cab that had brought him and fled into the Emergency Room, where police and attendants restrained him, sedated him, and stood beside the gurney as the physician on call examined him, ordered blood tests and X-rays, injected him with Penicillin, and sent him up to the eleventh floor in restraints with a diagnosis of pneumonia. He was burning up with fever.

As the fourth-year medical student on night duty, I tried to seem competent as I fumbled with the blood pressure apparatus and my stethoscope. The man (he seemed about 30 years old) kept gesturing wildly with his restrained arms at the window.

"Down there! They're in those four black limousines!"

I looked down eleven stories at the emergency entrance far below, but saw only the usual confusion of cars, taxis, and busses.

Piecemeal I gathered that he was being pursued by organized crime gang members bearing tommy guns, who were in four black limousines and were going to try to come into the hospital to kill him. With that scenario vividly in mind, I was thankful to realize that he was flagrantly paranoid and delusional.

Thankful also that I was only a medical student and not responsible for his management, I left him in care of the night nurse and went back to my chores in the laboratory.

Next morning, as required, I stood in his room with the small crowd of interns, residents, and the attending physician as they discussed his case and conversed with the man. His temperature was down.

"Do you remember those gangsters who were after you last night?"

The man hesitated, then said,

"I remember it all. I thought gangsters were after me. I thought they were trying to get up here in my room."

He laughed an embarrassed laugh.

"I must have been crazy!"

He went home in three days, back to his job as a competent civil servant.

NAKEDNESS IS NICE. CLOTHES ARE BETTER

Laurel, 4 years old, fought being dressed. She just didn't want to put on any clothes, ever. So her Mom decided to let her stay undressed. She didn't scold her, she didn't guilt-trip her, she just said, "OK."

Laurel spent two full days and nights of wild, free nakedness, then decided she liked to be dressed. There has been no problem since. Why fight against the lure of the forbidden? Why not just let her find out that nakedness is nice, but clothes are better?

NEEDS A NEW DADDY[13]

He is only two years and eleven months old, yet his face already has a fixed expression of anxiety. He moves stiffly, like a zombie. He climbs up and sits on the exam table without being asked.

Mom and Dad are separated. Dad (not present) is unemployed and drinks way too much coffee.

Mom explains, "He's petrified to go home with his Dad. He starts shaking and trembling and crying. It's a Jekyll and Hyde situation. For every little thing, his Dad's hand is up like this." She demonstrates Dad's threatening gesture.

"It's sad to watch him play. He takes his trucks and makes them talk to each other. The first truck says, 'I need a new Daddy.' The other truck says, 'Don't bother me. I'm busy.'"

"Yesterday he was eating a hot dog, and some relish dropped on the floor, and right away he was saying, 'It fell off, Mom, it fell off,' and he was afraid I was going to swat him. He continually keeps saying, 'I need a new Daddy.'"

I said to the boy, "You need a new Daddy. We'll have to think about that and see what we can do."

I said to the mother, "We're going to notify Protective Services right now."

---

13 This interaction can be viewed on the web at

www.higherlevelparenting.com. at Sect. II, Chapter 2, Module 17, "Scared of his Dad."

NINE YEARS OLD FOREVER

It was her ninth birthday and she was in for her regular checkup. She was in bouncing good health. Her mother had noticed the first hints of breast buds.

"What do you want to be when you grow up?" I asked.

Her reply was immediate, without hesitation.

"I want to be this old forever!" she said.

That was when I learned I had asked a stupid question.

NO HELP LUKE!

Luke's mother was one of those motherly mothers who wanted nothing more than to help her son with every difficulty in life. She was dedicated to easing his path at every stage. But Luke was one of those fiercely independent infants who want the thrill of personal victory over every difficulty. He shrank away from his loving mother whenever she approached. His very first sentence, enunciated in agonized tones, was, "No help Luke!"

I advised his mother to go with it, let him do things for himself.

Luke is now in college and still wants to do things for himself.

NOT QUITE PERFECT

He was one month old and up for adoption. His prospective parents, a young couple, were neatly dressed and well-mannered.

"We want you to give him a thorough and complete examination. If there is any defect, no matter how small, we are not going to adopt him."

I gave that baby a thorough examination. I pointed out that the cartilaginous contours of the left ear were not completely identical to those of the right ear. His posterior cranium was slightly asymmetrical. The palmar creases of the left hand were not identical to those of the right hand. The fifth fingers of each hand were slightly bent, resulting in a just-detectable tendency to clinodactyly. I thought he was a nice-looking kid, but definitely not perfect.

They thanked me for sparing them the inconvenience of adopting an imperfect human being.

ONE FLESH, ONE SPIRIT

Carol Gall

My husband had awakened in the middle of the night, not from the ubiquitous emergency phone calls from one of his many patients, but from a sense of personal dis-ease. He was severely nauseated. I got up to get a wastebasket for him to vomit into if he had to. He had to be sitting up to vomit, or he might swallow his own vomit, or choke on it, or aspirate it, but he was unable to sit up.

I didn't know until that very early morning how heavy a man feels when he is unable to move on his own. I was able to pull him into a sitting-up position, and he leaned over the bed, now not just feeling nauseated, but needing to vomit into the wastebasket I had fetched and lined with a large plastic bag. He could not support himself while leaning over the wastebasket, so I propped him up by leaning against the chest of drawers and holding him with my outstretched arms with all the force I could muster. When he was finished vomiting, I pushed him backward and he fell back into the bed. This process repeated itself numerous times.

I said I was going to call the ambulance, but he begged me not to. It was July 1. He said that this was the first day of the rotation of residents, and that he did not want to be treated in the middle of the night by a resident seeing his first emergency case. "But can't they call someone in?" He said, "There is no guarantee that they will, and more harm than good might be done by someone without experience."

"If we stay home, could anything bad happen?" I asked cautiously. He said, "No there isn't. In any case, I would rather stay home. There is nothing they can do for me at this point anyway. You can call them at 7 a.m. when the real doctors get in."

Calling an ambulance seemed to me to be the obvious choice, but I decided that my husband had been the successful captain of his own ship for many years and that he deserved to steer that ship on the route of his choice even if I felt panicked, which I did.

The hours passed by slowly until at last 7 a.m. arrived. I called our doctor at his home. (I had his home number since two of his children were my piano students.) He told me to call an ambulance and that he would meet me at the hospital.

Once in the hospital he was seen in the emergency room. I went out into the hall when the doctor started to leave the room, and when we were out of earshot of my husband, I asked him if I had done the right thing by waiting until 7 a.m. to call the ambulance. He said, "I would have told my wife the same thing. There is nothing we could have done for him in the vomiting stage that would have made any difference. I am sure he was more comfortable at home." I felt immensely relieved.

They scheduled him for a CAT scan. During the scan they detected early signs of stroke and they immediately took him out of the scan and prepped him for carotid artery surgery. The surgeon was on the way to the airport to visit his parents, who were themselves ailing, but he drove back to the hospital to do my husband's surgery.

During the surgery I prayed. As I was praying I felt the spirit of my husband making a decision. Was he to stay on this earth, or was he to progress to another dimension? It seemed that the decision was meant to be his alone, so I let my spirit step aside, so to speak, to allow his free will to make the decision without my "pulling" him to stay. I felt him make his decision, which was to remain on the earth, and was immensely relieved.

Not very much time elapsed, though it seemed like an eternity to me, when the surgeon came out to talk to me.

He said, "We almost lost him!"

I said, "I know!"

The surgeon gave me a look that was both compassionate and knowing, as if he had heard similar words from other spouses in the past, spouses who did, indeed, become "one flesh, one spirit", as the marriage vows intimate.

Because my husband had had the beginnings of a stroke in the CAT scan, it was determined that he would not go directly home, as many patients who receive carotid artery surgery do. He was kept in intensive care for several days.

At last he was discharged to our own home. At last we could sleep together in our own bed without all the interruptions to sleep caused by the hospital's routines. At last—peace, quiet, recovery time.

Alas, at two-thirty a.m. the phone rang. Who could possibly be calling us at this hour? Was it one of our four children in some kind of trouble? Was it my sister, or one of John's brothers?

The voice at the other end of the line asked for Dr. Gall.

I said, "Who is calling?"

She said, "This is Children's Hospital. We have a mother here who is hysterical. Dr. Gall is the only person we know of who can calm her down."

I said, "My husband has just gotten out of intensive care. This is our first night home. I don't want to wake him up! He is not on call."

Of course, my husband was already awake, conditioned as he was by the need to take phone calls during the night for the previous fifty years, but I wasn't about to disclose that.

She said, "But you don't understand. We need him to talk to this mother. She is hysterical!"

I said, "There are many doctors on staff. Let one of them do it."

She replied, "They have tried. Please, please put Dr. Gall on the line!"

Reluctantly, but proudly, I gave the phone to my husband. He talked to the mother in his soothing, hypnotic voice for about fifteen minutes. She calmed down completely and gave her permission for the hospital to treat the child she had brought to them. We went back to sleep.

A doctor is a doctor, first, foremost, and always.

ONE MORE MOLE

Most people have a few moles—ten or twenty, if you look carefully. A hundred or more qualifies as the big time. Most people don't care. They don't give them a second thought.

The patient was a strikingly beautiful teenager—a redhead who spent a lot of time on the beach. She knew doctors couldn't do anything about her freckles, but she could at least get her moles taken off.

She chose a young dermatologist just setting up practice in town. Full of energy and desire to impress his young patient, he removed her moles—over one hundred of them—at one sitting, and put them in a jar with preservative for later examination.

A week later his dilemma emerged. Under the microscope he saw that one of the moles was a malignant melanoma, a deadly form of cancer requiring immediate wide surgical excision.

But which spot on her body had it come from?

ONE, TWO, THREE . . .

Carol A. Gall

In our office we regularly saw children whose parents had scant financial resources. Usually these families lived in the small towns surrounding our metropolis, sometimes in rundown farmhouses, in apartments, or in mobile home parks. Housing was so expensive in the city itself that the service workers were often forced outside the city limits to find affordable housing for their families.

Our policy had been to send such families one or two bills, and if there was no response, we simply filed them in a separate file marked "Old Unpaid Bills."

At one point we had a financial manager who was unhappy with this approach. He decided to try to collect these unpaid bills, thinking our approach un-businesslike and a practice we could ill afford to continue in the face of declining revenues due to the HMO's.

Our business manager proceeded to call a woman to demand payment for services rendered to her five children. He was unaware that she had escaped with her car, her children, and her clothes from another state to get away from an abusive husband several years ago and was having a hard time making ends meet even with her full-time job. She had no education and her job paid barely more than minimum wage, so it was impossible for her to function adequately as the sole breadwinner for her family.

After receiving the call from our business manager, the mother called my husband in tears. He, of course, told her not to worry about the bills. We explained to the business manager that we preferred to leave things the way they had always been and directed him to cease trying to collect this type of bill. Our file of unpaid bills grew larger and larger. Some of the office staff resented our largesse, thinking us to be "enablers" of purposeful deadbeats.

One noon hour I was sitting at the receptionist's desk enjoying the relative quiet while the office staff was at lunch, and concentrating on the ever-present HMO forms. Usually no patients came in during our noon hour, but this day a young father in his late twenties came into the waiting room and approached the service window. He asked if he could come into the office, itself, and I opened the door for him.

He smiled the biggest, most buoyant smile I had ever seen and said to me, "You guys are great. We have not been able to pay our bills for quite awhile. We have had dunning phone calls and threatening letters during the entire time of our financial crisis. Except from you guys. I am paying you first!"

And with that he opened his billfold.

"One, two three, four, five hundred dollars!" he said as he handed me five one hundred dollar bills.

He put his billfold back into his pocket and started to leave.

"Wait!" I said. "Your bill is not quite that high. Let me get you your change."

With an even wider smile he said, "Keep it. You earned it!"

When we retired, we had a box of unpaid bills about a foot and a half long. The young man with his wide smile and his five hundred dollars was reward enough for all of those bills!

ORPHAN LOVE

When he arrived from Korea with his new American parents, he was nine months old. His entire life had been spent in an orphanage. Lying on the examination table, he refused to make eye contact. It wasn't a failure, it was an active refusal. He would jerk his eyes and then his entire head hard to the left or right to avoid making eye contact.

His parents brought him to me regularly for checkups and minor illnesses. With each visit he screamed and refused to interact.

When he was seven years old, he began to tolerate me.

When he was fifteen, his parents brought him in because he was having thoughts of suicide. He didn't know why, he said. He just felt that life was not worth living, and that he was worthless.

I sent him for counseling, with a prayer for his survival.

PARASITES AT TWO O'CLOCK

As interns at University Hospital in the 1950's, we dreamed of impressing our attending physicians by making a brilliant diagnosis of some rare and exotic disease. Most of us outgrew that adolescent day-dream but continued to respect the dedicated sleuthing required to pin down an elusive disorder.

The patient was a Washington notable, a high-ranking ambassador who traveled the world over on delicate diplomatic missions. Now he was in our hospital suffering from a mysterious fever of unknown origin. He seemed well enough during the day, except for a moderate anemia, but late at night, in the early morning hours, his temperature sky-rocketed to 104 degrees and higher. He shivered and chattered and shook until morning. He had the symptoms of infection with a tropical parasite, but repeated samples of his blood revealed nothing.

We didn't know the resident who solved the case. We were lowly interns and he was an exalted third-year medical resident. We only knew that he had bolted out of his bed at 2AM, grabbed a syringe and drawn a blood sample from his shivering patient.

Later, he explained. The ambassador's last assignment had been in Tahiti, many time zones away. The parasite typically produces a fever spike in the small hours of the night. The ambassador's doctors, reasoning that Washington, D.C., was twelve hours ahead of Tahiti, had been drawing blood for examination at noon—and finding nothing. The resident realized that the parasite swarms after the patient has been asleep for several hours. The patient's blood, drawn at two in the morning, was full of parasites.

REMEMBERING THE INCISION

Interns get little sleep. Getting waked up six, seven, eight or more times a night results in a zombie-like state in which it is hard to appear alert. The following day is spent in multiple micro-sleeps. Short-term memory suffers.

His aunt, only a few years older than himself and a vivacious Washington, D.C., reporter, has invited him to have lunch with her on the eleventh floor of the prestigious Washington Press Club. It's very informal. They line up cafeteria-style, aunt Winifred leading the way.

The line is slow. He drifts into revery and micro-sleep. He comes awake enough to realize that the young woman behind him is beckoning to him. She seems to know him, but he doesn't know her. She smiles a dazzling smile and he is aware how beautiful she is.

"Don't you remember me?" she asks. "You assisted the surgeon at my gall-bladder surgery last week."

Struggling to shake off his confusion, he looks again at her face, but recognition fails. Miserably trying to continue the conversation, he replies, perhaps too honestly,

"I don't remember your face, but I remember the incision very well."

He then devoutly wished that he could fall straight through the floor, all eleven stories, to the ground.

REPEAT AFTER ME . . .

That summer of 1953 I was a medical ROTC volunteer, serving an eight-week stint at a large eastern Army camp. I had chosen psychiatry as my field of interest as it seemed to be the one area about which I had the most questions. I felt I needed to know a great deal more about this thing called mental illness.

My task was to conduct interviews and then dictate summaries of my findings. I had no clue as to how to do this, but I had heard someone say that the way to proceed was to reflect back to the patient his own last few words.

The patient was a young man in process of being discharged from medical service for psychiatric reasons.

"I'm being kicked out on a Section Eight," he said.

"Section Eight," I said.

"You know—looney," he said.

"Looney," I said.

"This chicken Army," he said. "Do this, do that, always being ordered around."

"Ordered around," I said.

"Yeah, ordered around. Just like my old man."

"Just like your old man."

Suddenly there was a change in his manner. He whirled around to face me, eyes blazing.

"My old man. If I had a gun right now, I'd kill him!"

For the next hour it poured out of him, the years of mistreatment at home and the smoldering rage that mistreatment had engendered. I was frightened. I thought he might actually go berserk and attack me.

I had not the remotest idea of what to do or say, so I did nothing, said nothing, and he gradually subsided. At the end of the hour, he thanked me.

"Thanks, doc, for listening. You're the only person that listened."

That was the day I learned that psychiatry is something more than a clever verbal formula.

SEND MORE CYLERT[14]

A young divorced woman came to see my late wife Beth and me. She was in a crisis. She had a daughter eleven years old who had been diagnosed as hyperactive at the age of four years. She had been seen by a total of five psychiatrists and psychologists, all of whom agreed that she was organically hyperactive and lacking in impulse control. She had been placed on Ritalin, amphetamines, you name it, in doses high enough to make a zombie out of a 200 pound adult. No improvement. Teachers sent home notes saying, "Send more Cylert!"

The mother was trying to sell her house. Zoey had gone up in the attic and trampled through the ceiling of the bedroom. Chunks of plaster and clouds of plaster dust sifted down into the bedroom. It cost several hundred dollars just to get the mess cleaned up, and as soon as the workmen had finished the cleanup, Zoey had gone up in the attic and done the whole job over again. The mother was afraid she was going to kill her own daughter.

I told her I would take the case, but she would have to commit herself in advance to carry out my instructions fully and completely, even if she didn't understand what they were all about. Puzzled but desperate, she agreed.

Her ex-husband, who lived in another state, was trying to get custody of Zoey and Mother was fighting him bitterly on this. I told her to say nothing to the girl, but to call her ex-husband and tell him she had decided to let him have the girl. She was to pack Zoey's clothes while she was asleep and put them in the car, then the next morning tell Zoey that she could skip school, they were going on a trip. When she got to her ex-husband's place, she was to leave the girl and her baggage off without any explanation and drive home alone. All of Zoey's medications were to be dumped down the toilet, every last

---

14 Reported in *Elegant Parenting*, 1994

pill, and no more medication was to be given.

Three weeks later a very puzzled school counselor called me to ask why I wanted a report from him about Zoey. She was a model student, making all A's. Was there some problem that he didn't know about? I told him, "No, no problem."

Six weeks later the girl's father called. The girl was happy. Could he keep her a while longer? I advised the mother to say, "Yes."

Six months later Zoey won a National Merit Scholarship. Once every month or so she wrote a happy letter to her mother, signing it with her love.

Later that year Dad got a new girl friend. Zoey's school performance went down. She decided she really liked Mom better, after all. She asked to go back to Mom. Dad said, "OK."

Five years later the mother was happily remarried. Zoey was OK with that.

Fifteen years later the family agreed to be present at a conference sponsored by the University. Zoey, now a college graduate, was presented as an example of the erroneous diagnosis of hyperactivity. Her present occupation? Elementary school teacher!

Seven years of treatment with stimulant drugs. A four-year-old placed on stimulant drugs! Five psychiatrists and psychologists. Seven years of being called hyperactive. And the cure was to dump her medications down the toilet and send her back to Daddy.

SHEEP SHEARS

I was one of two pediatricians in a large Pennsylvania clinic, not far from Amish country.

A five day old baby was admitted with florid tetanus, in the throes of massive spasms. It was hard to watch him die.

Sturdy Amish folk they were, husband and wife. She delivered their first baby at home, and he, summoned from the barn, had used the sheep shears to cut the cord.

SINUS TROUBLE

Her Dad brought her in because she was sniffing and blowing her nose more than usual, and he thought she might have a sinus problem. I asked her to sit on the examining table. I examined her ears, nose, and throat, and checked lymph nodes in her neck.

As I explained to Dad that she didn't really seem to have much in the way of sinus findings, I listened to her heart and lungs and absent-mindedly gestured for her to lie down on the examining table.

My right hand was gently palpating her liver and spleen when it struck something rock-hard, right in the middle of her abdomen. It felt like a piece of concrete, and it seemed to be firmly attached to her spine.

It was a big benign tumor, a ganglioneuroma, hard to remove completely, but the surgeons got it out, and it never came back.

After that I became very wary of ever doing a partial physical examination of any patient. Part of a doctor's brain is in his hands, and he must use them if he is to find out what he needs to know.

SKINNY BABY

My late wife, Beth, became famous as the consultant of last resort for difficult breast-feeding problems, but this one stumped even her for a while. It wasn't really a breast-feeding problem, it was a post-breast-feeding problem.

The mother's little boy had transitioned very smoothly to solid foods. He enjoyed sitting in his new high chair, trying out the wonderful new world of flavors and textures being offered to him. Nevertheless, he was failing to gain weight. With each passing week he got skinnier and skinnier. Mother and Beth went over his diet carefully, noting variety and nutritive values and portion sizes. Nothing seemed wrong.

Beth played her final card. She made a house visit. There, in the dinette area, was the baby, sitting in his high chair, cheeks and bib smeared with food, crowing happily. Crouched just next to the high chair was the family dog—a very fat family dog—looking up expectantly for his next handout. Baby was enthusiastically feeding the dog.

In just two weeks the dog was thinner, the baby fatter.

SMALL IS BEAUTIFUL

She was the smallest preemie ever to survive at University Hospital. At 640 grams, she was tiny enough to fit in the palm of your hand. She spent many months in the incubator, just growing bigger, before she was allowed to go home with her mother.

Regular tests were done to monitor her hearing, her vision, her mental status. Her brain was scanned for signs of bleeding. Developmental tests were done every few months. No signs of abnormality were detected. Everyone involved held their breath.

Her regular checkups remained normal. By two years of age she was in the normal range for height and weight. Her attachment to her parents was normal. She played with her dolls. She laughed and chattered, enjoyed jokes and make-believe. Her vocabulary grew and grew. Her face displayed an extraordinary range of emotions. In repose it shone with an inner light that in a mature adult would have been called by the name of Wisdom.

By the time she was five years old, it had become plain for all to see that she was a born actress, not an ordinary actress, but one of those rare human beings who can experience and project to others the full range of human experience.[15]

---

15 To view this interaction, go to www.higherlevelparenting.com, section II-17, "Osmosis."

SMITTY AND THE CAT

Carol Gall

People often ask me how my husband, John, and I first met. It is quite a story.

I do hands-on healing and have done for more than thirty years. It is an odd world to be involved with, to say the least, populated by more kooks, I sometimes think, than legitimate practitioners of healing arts or seekers. To try to add legitimacy to my own work, I wanted to do healing meditations for a doctor who didn't believe in what I do, with patients I had never met who were referred by that doctor, with no more information than first name, age, sex, and condition. I hoped for feedback biased in the opposite direction, that is, feedback from a skeptic. If I got verifiable results under those conditions, I felt I would be affirmed regarding my own abilities.

One of my best friends was a pianist and organist. We had met when we both taught in the same studios twenty-five years earlier. Besides the commonality of music, we had both adopted children at about the same time. One day when we were talking, I lamented the lack of a doctor who would fit the bill for my needs.

To my surprise she said, "I have the doctor for you!"

Her sister, who had passed away a year ago from multiple myeloma, had been married to John Gall, a pediatrician, for thirty-five years. *He* would be the perfect person, she thought. She gave me his unlisted phone number.

I called him, and outlined my proposition. He was most polite, but entirely uninterested. He did give me the name of a colleague with whom I collaborated for a few months, and I forgot about John for a while.

However, something, I don't know what, compelled me to call him again. This time I identified myself as a friend of his late wife's sister, and expressed condolences for his recent loss. I think he didn't connect me with my prior call at that time. Much to my surprise he called me back in a couple of days and we chatted.

We found that we had many interests in common, such as classical music, psychology, and the behaviors of children, and it was quickly apparent to us both that we were used to thinking "out of the box." I especially liked that he affirmed some of the decisions I had made regarding my children, against the advice of "experts" who were weighing in at the time. I found that he had written a whole chapter in his book "Elegant Parenting" entitled "Lemmings are Consistent!" (Lemmings consistently fall to their death—an analogy to his thoughts about consistency in parenting!) We both felt that each circumstance had a uniqueness to it that made consistency irrelevant many times, or that the "surprise" factor of changing what one did from time to time actually had better results with children than the time-honored idea of consistency.

Soon we both had three hundred dollar a month phone bills. Sometimes he read from Dr. Milton Erickson, a psychiatrist who was skilled in the use of trance states, something which I used myself in doing healing. By now he remembered the first call, but did not lump me with the "kooky" element, much to my relief.

One day I summoned up all my courage and called him at our five a.m. time (four a.m. for me, which was difficult for me, a night person, but the time he had invited me to call) and I happened to wake him up.

I told him I had something I wished to tell him.

He said, "I need to brush my teeth first. Hold the line."

Holding the line, I nearly lost my courage, but I managed to say, "I think I love you, John!"

He responded in kind, and a few days later he asked, "Will you marry me?"

I said, "Yes!" and he replied, "I guess it's time we meet."

He made arrangements to come to the Cities on the afternoon of September 6, 1994, and I went to the airport to meet him. This was prior to all the security that ensued after 9/11, so I was in the concourse where his plane was to land a few minutes before the appointed time.

The plane he was supposed to be on arrived and passengers began to disembark. John had sent me a picture of him, so I had at least some idea of what he might look like. Passengers streamed off the airplane, but no relatively short, sixty-eight year old grey haired man walked off that airplane.

The flight attendants disembarked, followed by the pilots. Still no one who looked like John's picture had come off the airplane. I thought maybe he had changed his mind about coming, or that he had missed his plane due to some child's medical emergency and hadn't had a chance to call.

Just as I was about to give up and was feeling very sad and deflated, a small, tired looking man got off the plane, bobbing his head left and right, scanning the people in the concourse, looking for a woman who would match the picture I had sent to him.

We met, confirmed our identities, and started to walk toward the baggage claim area. He took my hand and squeezed it (he claims it was the other way around) and a surge of electricity pulsed through my body. I knew we were going to be just fine!

I learned later that he almost always gets off airplanes last. He doesn't like getting jostled.

We drove to the duplex I was renting after selling my home, and I made scallops with creamed garlic sauce for our supper, a bull's eye as far as he was concerned. The next morning I made him a Dutch pancake, another bull's eye. He hadn't told me that his favorite ingredients were eggs, butter, and cream, the main ingredients in a Dutch pancake, not to mention the garlic cream sauce that had graced the scallops!

We spent our short time together—he left the morning of September 9—meeting my two boys, seeing the sights, and endlessly talking about out interests and our lives. We set our wedding date, October 29, 1994. I would come to Michigan September 30 to live and work on our wedding—there were flowers to order, invitations to choose and get out, a reception to organize—all in less than a month's time after arrival!

In the meantime he returned to Michigan. He had planned a trip to Stratford, Ontario with his two grown boys plus his brother and sister-in-law. We would be incommunicado for a whole week.

I received a request from friends of mine who owned a bed and breakfast to come and stay for that week, which included the Labor Day weekend. They hadn't had a vacation in years, and needed someone to care for their eleven-year-old daughter, whom I had tutored the past school year. She was profoundly mentally retarded, but I had taught her 57 words and also toilet trained her that past year. I eagerly accepted, especially since it would make the time go faster for me. Anyway, I enjoyed working with Melinda.

Inadvertently, I learned a new strategy for working with this type of child.

Of course, I spent a massive amount of time interacting with Melinda during our long weekend together. We practiced the words cards we had worked on earlier, I taught her a couple of new words, prepared meals, went to the grocery store, got her baths started, put her to bed with a bedtime story, etc.

From time to time, however, I would drift off into a reverie about my new life, wondering how it would change, what Michigan would be like, what kind of wedding we would have...

Never had Melinda had anything other than my undivided attention when we were together, and never before had I given her the "brush off," so to speak, when she indicated she wanted my attention.

She finally came and pulled on me, sat down, and gently pulled me down with her. This from a child who had been content in the past to twirl a scarf, or engage in other self-stimulating acts for hours at a time!

Her mother said to me later, "I don't know what you did with her, but now she won't leave us alone! She demands our attention and is now a part of the family in a way that she has never been before!

Imagine that! A reverie turned into an intervention!

Eventually the appointed time, September 30, arrived. I left the Cities at five in the morning. John met me at the Detroit airport and we drove to his—now our—home. I had forgotten how bachelors live. I opened up the freezer compartment of the refrigerator that first day and saw what looked like long, frozen worms. "What is that!" I exclaimed. He said, "Frozen spaghetti. I make it up on Sunday night and freeze six days worth. Then when I get home from work all I have to do it put the noodles in boiling water, heat up a little Newman's Own Sockarooni sauce, and supper is ready!" No wonder he had found my scallops and Dutch pancake so appealing!

Of course, all was not totally smooth in our relationship. We had to get to know one another differently than we had been able to do in the past. We had not dated. We had only spoken by phone.

He had everything in neat piles all over the house, and I didn't like the clutter. The living room was stuffed full of furniture so that it looked like a furniture warehouse rather than someone's inviting living room. And on one wall was wallpaper from the floor to the ceiling of a north woods lake scene, fine for a postcard, but not for a living room, in my view. I would start projects and didn't finish them before starting another, leaving a chaotic mess rather than his neat piles.

And in some important ways we were like Smitty and the neighbor's cat.

Smitty had been his family dog for many years, and had died before I met John, but John had loved Smitty and had told me many stories about him. Smitty was a lovely dog, a friendly dog, and the neighbors had an equally friendly cat.

The cat would come into John's backyard, and the dog would run to the cat and wag its tail. The cat would look disgusted and run back into his own yard. Cats, of course, wave their tails when they are angry, not when they are happy. Some days the cat would run over to Smitty and playfully bat at his nose. Smitty would run as fast as he could the other way. The two animals, despite many tries, never quite bridged the gap between them, never understood the other's body language.

John and I were like that. He liked Milton Erickson. I hadn't read Milton Erickson, but I like Erik Erikson, who wrote books like "Childhood and Society" and "Young Man Luther." John liked Eric Byrne's books on transactional analysis. I, on the other hand, had rejected the books, which I had had to read in graduate school, as banal. "The language is so simplistic!" I complained. "I like to read Erik Erikson. He uses language around which one can wrap one's mind."

Then there was what became the infamous tape.

I had attended a symposium a few years before and one of the presenters was a medium who became unconscious, much as Edgar Cayce did, "channeled" information, and had no memory of it upon awakening. John was intrigued by Edgar Cayce, and I was eager to play him my tape, thinking he would see the connections. One of the "entities" this woman channeled gave lots of predictions about where medical science would be going in the next years, and I thought John would enjoy it.

However, the first entity she channeled this particular night was one that I had not been able to process myself.

It began in a loud voice, "From the bowels of the earth—" and that was all John would listen to. He began to cry. I could see that he wondered if I was even sane, if I were drawn to that type of thing. I put the tape away and have not played it since.

I longed for a chance to redeem myself, in his eyes. That chance seemed to come the day he got a migraine headache.

John had been plagued by migraines since he could remember. As a child, cigar smoke or the smell of cabbage cooking would cause their onset. As an adult he was unsure of what the triggers were exactly, but once a migraine began it disabled him. He had to go to bed in a darkened room, bothered by the slightest noise or ray of light. Usually they lasted two days, and required him to cancel his patients and any social events planned.

Then Cardizem came onto the market. It was apparently developed as a calcium-channel blocker for high blood pressure, but for a fortunate few, Cardizem blocked migraine pain. His life was at last normal.

The insurance company mandated that it would pay for a generic version of Cardizem, and for whatever reason—the green dye, perhaps—on the very first day he tried it, it didn't work. He got a full-fledged migraine.

He sat at the dining room table unable to eat his supper and bemoaning his fate. I said, "I know how to do migraines! Will you please let me try to help you?"

At that point he probably would have agreed to most any intervention, however slim the chance of success. So I put my hands on his temples and jaw, then over his eyes, his forehead.

He asked me, "What are you seeing?"

Usually I don't see anything, but this day I "saw" the migraine, and I explained its progress.

"Oh my God!" He said. "That is just what you see on an MRI!"

I continued to work on him, until in twenty minutes time he was pain free. He felt weak and washed out, but was pain free.

I couldn't have been happier. At last I had redeemed myself in his eyes! We didn't speak about it until a month later, when I brought it up.

I couldn't believe his response. He said he had no memory of the incident whatsoever. I was furious! "So much for science!" I declared angrily. "If something doesn't fit your preconceived notions, you can't even remember it!"

We were definitely behaving like Smitty and the cat, growling and hissing at one another.

I often accompanied John in the exam room as he examined children. One day a six-year-old boy came in who had broken his arm in three places. A bone was sticking up where it should not have been, but had not broken the skin. We felt that he should have been at the orthopedic surgeon's office getting an x-ray, but the rules of his HMO stated that he had to be seen by the primary care physician first. So there he was, with his helpless mother, in pain, forced to make a side trip to us before he could get the relief he needed.

John decided to give him some liquid pain medication, since he was unable to swallow pills, but we were all out of it. He sent one of our nurses around to other doctors in our medical building, but no one had any.

John said in a low voice I had never heard before, "Well, my wife might be able to help!" And with that he opened the exam room door, and shut it, heading for his desk in his adjacent office.

I was still angry about the migraine incident, and I found myself thinking, "Coward!" But at the same time I knew he was giving me a chance to help this child with my abilities, and I was anxious to help.

I told the child I thought that together we could ease his pain. "I will put my hands over your arm, but I won't touch you. I will help the pain to leave your arm, but I don't want to take it all. Otherwise you might re-injure yourself."

I asked him to close his eyes.

"What color is the pain?" I inquired.

He answered, "Brown."

I said, "Keep looking at that brown in your arm and let it come out into my hand."

I felt, as I always do, an "energy block" that proceeded to come out of his injured arm and into my hand.

I "broke" the block and he said, "Okay, you can stop now. It doesn't hurt now!"

I walked over to his mother, put my hands on her forehead, removed them shortly thereafter and she declared, "My headache is gone!"

The two of them left, puzzled, but happy, and I related to John what had happened.

Much later I tried to give John an attunement so that he, also, could feel energy in the way that I can. He couldn't. He was my only failure to date.

I am happy to report that after twelve and a half years of marriage I redid the attunement and he is now able to feel energy. I don't think he particularly wants to use it, at least not to the extent that I do, but he now knows what I am talking about, that it is, indeed, a physical sensation.

We are still somewhat like Smitty and the cat, but we are closer to understanding that a cat's tail and a dog's tail mean opposite things, and the batting cat's paw is a friendly gesture!

SOME SERIOUS COUGHING

Joey was ten years old when he came home from school one day and walked into the living room to find his twelve year old sister on the floor, wrapped in a sheet and apparently dead. She had been hit by a car.

Actually, she was only bruised and recovered quickly. But Joey woke up at 4 AM the next morning and ran to the bathroom, retching and gagging. Over the next few days he developed a bronchitis which did not respond to antibiotics, and because of continued coughing, his doctors thought he might have aspirated something when he vomited. He was put in the hospital and bronchoscoped.

Nothing was found, but he continued to cough. After several months, he was bronchoscoped again and again nothing was found. His cough became worse. It was a loud, barking, brassy, echoing cough that startled people and it occurred with great regularity every ten seconds. He was brought to University Hospital, where a third bronchoscopy was performed with negative results. As he recovered from the anesthetic, he again resumed coughing. He was brought directly to me from the hospital.

I told Joey that I had calculated how much coughing he was doing and at the present rate of 6 times a minute, 12 hours a day, he was coughing about four thousand times a day or over a hundred thousand times a month--about a million times a year. In fifty years, he could probably expect to cough about fifty million times.

It was therefore very important to keep a record of his coughing so that we could tell if he was improving or getting worse. I instructed him to get a spiral-bound notebook and a pencil and carry it with him everywhere and be sure to record all coughs when they occurred. I showed him how to make four check marks and then a fifth check mark through the preceding four. He was to divide up the pages into columns and be sure to record anything that was happening at the time that might be affecting his cough.

He looked at me knowingly and said, "You're just trying to use psychology on me!"

I agreed that that was true but added that his coughing was a serious matter and it was therefore important to pay attention and keep a record of his coughs and would he please do it. He agreed to do it.

Four days later his mother called to say that his coughing had practically stopped. Five years later he has not had any more trouble with coughing.

Three hospitalizations. Three bronchoscopies. Three anesthesias. Many months of unnecessary antibiotic treatment, not to mention the anxiety of thinking about serious lung disease.

And Joey could not deny that his cough was a serious symptom, and therefore it was a serious matter that he keep an accurate record of his coughing. And the problem was solved by means of those few words: a *serious matter* and *an accurate record.*

STOMACHACHES THREE TIMES A DAY[16]

She was a big thirteen-year-old girl, healthy in every way. She got along well with her sister and her mother and father. Her problem was not really severe. It wasn't messing up her life. It had been going on a long time and wasn't getting any worse, but Mom couldn't understand what it was all about and had finally decided to come in to the pediatrician to get a diagnosis.

It was stomachaches, three times a day. They came at the same time every day: at seven-thirty in the morning, after she had gotten up and brushed her teeth; a half-hour before noon; and again at five-thirty in the afternoon. They lasted less than half an hour.

They were a well-organized and well-disciplined family, well-organized and well-disciplined for work and for play according to well-established principles of industrial efficiency. The schedule of activities for each family member was written out each week, in advance. Menus were written out in advance, and meals were served promptly on schedule.

I inquired of the girl, "How do you know when to eat?"

She replied, "I look at the clock. We always eat on time."

"How do you know if you're hungry?"

She blinked in bewilderment. "By the clock, of course."

We talked about hunger pangs. In a household run by the clock, she had never connected the strange feelings in her stomach with the need to eat.

16 From *Elegant Parenting*, 1994

SUPER ASPIRIN

The town of Ekalaka, it was said, came into existence when an itinerant purveyor of hard liquors got his wagon stuck trying to cross the stream bed there and decided to set up shop on the spot, estimating, perhaps rightly, that any place in Montana was as good as any other for selling hard liquor.

Ekalaka prospered about as well as any place in Montana, that is to say, hardly at all. It became relatively famous when someone discovered dinosaur tracks there, but nothing else of any significance had happened in the past fifty years.

The doctor in Ekalaka had a patient with measles who wasn't getting better, and he asked for a pediatric consultation.

Our little clinic didn't get many requests for consultation. It was easier just to send a patient over to us. We asked our clinic manager how to deal with this request.

"It's fifty miles. Charge them fifty dollars."

For fifty dollars I would drive to Ekalaka and look at a sick kid with the measles.

When I got there I saw why the doctor had asked for a consultation. The boy was in an oxygen tent. His body was covered with big purplish measles spots. His temperature was over 104 degrees. A chest X-ray showed pneumonia.

Why was he so sick from measles?

I re-examined him. I re-checked his medical record. I looked at his medications. He was getting antibiotics and aspirin. I looked again at the aspirin bottle. It wasn't plain aspirin. It was aspirin plus cortisone. This child was getting steroids!

I recommended stopping the steroid-laced aspirin.

Next day the doctor called to say the child was improving.

TAKE A DEEP BREATH

John Gall

It happens every year, in some classroom in the local school system. A child is diagnosed with head lice, and panicked parents by the dozen call for scalp medication.

This call was different. As a public service, this Mom was recommending that we tell other mothers to use mayonnaise on their child's hair, because the lice had become resistant to the commonly used pediculicides.

"Oh, how so?" The receptionist was curious.

"The lice have learned how to hold their breath until the medicine is washed out," Mom replied.

Carol Gall

It was at last lunchtime. We had a fully equipped kitchen in our lounge, and I heated up some homemade soup that I had brought from home for my husband and me. Both of us enjoyed our food, and as I found cooking relaxing after a long day at the office followed by teaching piano students, I soon had steaming hot oxtail soup I had prepared the night before poured into bowls for the two of us.

Of course, the telephone beeped at me just as I was about to take my first swallow. It was my job to answer whatever calls came in during the noon hour break so that nurses could get some peace.

"Liberty Pediatrics," I said wearily. "How can I help you?"

The person at the other end of the line said, "Hello! I am Ardis Mansfield, the school nurse at the Oak Street School. Dr. Gall is our liaison medical person and we are to call him in an emergency!" I braced myself for some catastrophe, supposing that whatever it was she had to tell me would inevitably result in a disruption of our patient schedule for the afternoon and most probably meant an end to our often shortened noon "hour."

"Yes," I answered. "I am aware of our responsibility to your school. How can we help you?"

She replied, "We are having an epidemic of lice at the Oak Street School." There was a long pause. "I read an article on the internet that the treatment doctors give has no effect."

"Why did the article say it has no effect?" I queried.

" Because the shampoo which has the medication in it can't possibly work. You are supposed to leave it on thirty minutes. The instructions say not to leave the shampoo on for longer than thirty minutes, as it can damage the scalp."

"Yes," I said affirming her statement.

"Well, lice have adapted themselves to that," she continued. "They can hold their breath for thirty minutes."

I began to laugh. I laughed for over a minute and tried to speak, but could not, and every time I tried to say something I would start to laugh all over again. I laughed for several minutes before I finally could say, "Don't worry, dear. It won't matter. Lice don't have lungs! The treatment was designed for such a creature as that. It *will* kill the lice. Just make sure that the families treat everyone infected, washing all the bedding, couches and anywhere else someone's head may have lain so that they are not re-infected after the treatment!"

I went back to our table hardly able to tell my husband about the incident, as I was still laughing. Ah, sweet and rare justice prevailed in that I was, indeed, able to eat my oxtail soup without further interruption!

TALK TO THE DOG.

Elissa, 19 months old, fought being placed in the car seat and fought being removed from it.

One day, Mom decided to let her stay in the car seat. Mom got out of the car, rolled down the car window, closed the car doors, and went in the house (looking out to check on Elissa).

Elissa continued to talk happily to the family dog, who was in the car with her, then looked out the car window and called, "All done!" She was quite happy to be removed from the car seat. She really just wanted some time to talk to the dog.

TALK TO THE PIG

Carol Gall

Rodney, age fifteen, was severely handicapped mentally. He had never learned how to talk. Although I had had extensive training to help severely handicapped patients, I nevertheless worked with him for several months without success.

One day, making no progress, as usual, I decided to take Rodney with me for a walk down the neighborhood street. After all, there was little point in staying indoors and grinding away unsuccessfully.

There was a garage sale going on a few blocks down. A pet pig, one of those dainty, swaybacked pigs, was on display. When Rodney saw the pig, he rushed over to its cage and began an animated conversation with the pig. He was using the King's English!

Thereafter, whenever I needed to show Rodney's parents how well he was progressing, I arranged a visit with the pig.

TEN-CENT DOCTOR

The baby was already dying on admission to the emergency room. His skin was pale and covered with uncountable bluish spots—a hemorrhagic rash. His blood pressure was undetectable. We raced to start intravenous antibiotics, massive doses of steroids. No use. It was Waterhouse-Friderichsen syndrome—massive adrenal failure secondary to uncontrollable infection with meningococcus.

We broke the news to his father, who had taken him to his local physician six hours ago.

"All he did was give him a shot of penicillin and send us home."

His face was twisted in agony. "Those ten-cent doctors!"

How could we tell him that his baby was already doomed, even before he went to the doctor?

THAT'S MY HANG-GLIDER[17]

Our son Duane had been in the basement for twelve years learning how to make model airplanes. He didn't want to imitate his younger brother and fly airplanes. He wanted to be a hang-glider person!

One day he came home with this mass of bolts and screws and rods and Nylon. At first we thought he had brought home a piece of a sailboat.

I said, "What on earth is that?"

He said, "Dad, that's my hang-glider. I'm gonna be a hang-glider person!"

I don't know if you've ever experienced that sinking feeling, but it's an awful feeling—Oh, my God!

He said, "I've saved my money. I've saved twenty five hundred dollars and I bought this and it's mine, and I want you to see how beautiful it is. So will you come out in the back yard with me and let me show you as I assemble it."

I said, "Well, sure." I didn't let him see how pale my face was.

We went out into the back yard, and he proceeded to put this thing together from three o'clock to four o'clock and from four o'clock to five o'clock and from five o'clock to six o'clock. We sat there and the sun went across the sky and set. We turned on the back yard lights and there was this gigantic bat-like creature growing in the twilight.

When he got it all put together he said, "Here's what you do. You lie right here"—with that leather strap—"and then you can fly!"

I said, "Wow!"

It was too dark that night, so he dismantled it and put it away.

---

17 First published in *Elegant Parenting*, 1994.

Then a few days later the opportunity came and he said, "Take me down to the golf course, because I want to show you how this thing flies, it's really neat."

We went to tee number seventeen or thereabouts, where you tee off and there's a cliff—suicide hill!

He put it together right there on the tee-off and got into it, strapped himself in, backed up all the way back so as to get a good running start, and he ran—again it was about twilight—he ran and leaped off the cliff.

And the thing flew! And I could just see what an experience this was for him. It was only about a half inch off the ground, but it was flying. Maybe he got up to a foot or two. Then it ran out of wind and it came to the ground. It hit really hard and bent the struts. Duane was thrown forward onto the ground. He didn't break anything, but he was out of breath. He stood up and he said, "See! It flies!"

I said, "That's great!" It was too dark to try again, so we went home and a couple of days later he announced he was going to take it up to Sleeping Bear Dunes.

Fortunately there was a cold snap that Fall and he didn't actually get to take it up there, and did we feel relieved! Winter set in, and he rolled up the hang glider and put it in the garage.

But that winter he fell in love. He met the girl that he later married. And the courtship proceeded very quickly. It was only a few weeks until he had reached the stage of bringing her home to introduce her to the family and show her around the family estate—all quarter acre of it.

He was proudly doing this with Barbara when they came to the garage. She looked up and saw this thing and she said, "What's that?"

"Oh, that's my hang-glider!"

There was a long silence from the garage, and then we heard the fatal words.

She said, "Death-toy! Either it goes or I go!"

That was the end of that. He never touched it again. It rotted in place. That was the end of hang-gliding.

Duane went on to become a champion model airplane racer, a designer of racing model airplanes, an editor of the model racers' magazine, an organizer of model racing societies.

You don't ask them to obey you when they are young adults. What you do is let them show you what they can do. But you can let somebody else come in and tell them a thing or two.

THE DANCE BEGINS AT BIRTH

As a pediatrician, I routinely ask mothers of new babies at 1, 2, or 3 days of age whether they are talking with their babies. Some mothers don't understand the question, but others respond enthusiastically.

"Oh, yes," they say. "We have long conversations." And they proceed to demonstrate for me.

It's amazing to watch a tiny baby initiate a conversation with a grownup by waving his arms and legs in a certain way, raising his eyebrows, and making certain sounds. True, it's not the King's English, but, believe me, it's very effective.

My point is, the textbooks say babies don't talk until maybe six, seven or eight months of age. The textbooks miss almost the entire phenomenon of human communication in infancy by using an arbitrary adult definition of talking. They are blocked by their a priori assumptions, by a certain way of thinking adopted in advance of observing the phenomenon. Mothers down through the ages have known how to talk to their babies, but if you go to medical school and read the textbooks, you will not know that it ever happens. Worse yet, you will believe that you know that it doesn't happen.

If that early communication between mother and infant is not properly established in the right way and at the right time, the infant moves on to the next chronological level of development without having had the experiences and without having gained the skills appropriate to the earlier level. The result is likely to be a severe and lifelong handicap in the process of growing up. It is our task to see to it that disturbances of early communication and learning of whatever nature are detected and corrected or, better yet, prevented. We cannot do that if we have a definition of communication that leaves out the first and most crucial six months.

Because it is a problem of correctly perceiving the problem itself, I call it a meta-problem. If you have misperceived the problem, what is your chance of getting the right solution?

THE DARK SIDE[18]

Lily had been doing a lot of baby-talk and wetting her pants. Mom thought she was feeling ambivalent about being a big girl, so to give her big-girl privileges, she bought her some children's scissors.

Lily promptly used them to cut up a doll quilt that Grandma had made for her. Mom just was sick about it. Nice straight lines, she cut right along the lines! It was all over the rug and over the floor, all in pieces.

Mom just started crying. Lily was real upset that Mom was upset. She put her arm around Mom and said, "Never mind, Mom! I have other blankets to keep my dolls warm!"

Mom told her, "Well, honey, this was special because Grandma made it. This was something special. You don't want to cut up things like this, this was real special."

Lily said, "Ohh!" She still had her arm around Mom.

"Ohh!" She was patting Mom's back—"I didn't know Grandma made this! I thought *you* made that, Mom!"

Mom was speechless. Mom didn't know what else to say.

18 Reported in *Elegant Parenting*, 1994

THE GIRL WHO SLEPT FOR A YEAR[19]

The girl (call her Sue) was in high school. She was popular, an excellent student, had lots of friends her own age. Her father was a psychiatrist, a wise and insightful man; her mother a warm, loving, motherly person. Sue returned to school for her sophomore year after a wonderful summer and came down with the same virus that afflicted half her class. She spent a week in bed, then went back to school and promptly pooped out. She spent another week in bed, tried again to go back to school, pooped out again. Her classmates by this time were all back in school and functioning normally. Her parents brought her to see me.

Her physical exam was normal. Her laboratory studies were normal. She was not depressed. She didn't have any personal or family problems. I thought perhaps she had post-viral fatigue and recommended another two weeks at home. She stayed in bed another two weeks, then pooped out again.

Her father was worried; so was I. I was pretty sure she didn't have anything seriously wrong with her, but pretty sure isn't always enough. Her father suggested we consult with his University colleagues in neurology, psychiatry, endocrinology, hematology. Sue had EEG's, brain imaging, and extensive laboratory tests. Nothing turned up.

I recommended that she be allowed to continue sleeping every day for as long as she felt the need. She slept all fall, all winter, all spring. She ate three meals a day, didn't lose any weight, remained cheerful and without symptoms. She did enough studying at home to keep up with her class. Dad had her re-examined by his colleagues. Nothing turned up.

Later the second summer she gradually regained her old vivacity. She went back to school without incident, graduated from high school, and went on to a successful career in college. She never felt unduly sleepy again.

19 First published in the Senior Bulletin of the American Academy of Pediatrics, Fall, 2007.

Strange things happen in adolescence. They are not necessarily symptoms of disease or psychological disorder. They test the skill and tact of the physician to the utmost to avoid pathologizing a normal if unusual process.

THE GRAVE-DIGGER'S DAUGHTER

There she was, sitting up in a hospital bed in Gallinger Hospital, the charity hospital for the District of Columbia. She was a rather normal appearing teenager except for her huge neck. We students listened, awe-struck, as the attending physician explained.

"She's one of the lucky ones," he said. "A lot of them choke to death. You're looking at a recovering case of diphtheria. That membrane grows in their throat and chokes off their airway. The inflammation makes a brawny edema of the neck that gives them that bull-neck appearance. Maybe her throat was just big enough to accommodate the membrane and still have a little airway left. She never got her baby shots."

But where did she come in contact with a case of diphtheria? Where did she catch it?

"It's right here on the chart. She's the daughter of the hospital gravedigger. He buries a lot of diphtheria victims."

THE HEALING PATH

I have heard a person say, "I've been accepted to medical school. I'm going to take my M.D. Then I will take my residency, then my subspecialty training, then I will go into practice."

I know that such a person is planning to take his M.D., to take his internship, then take his residency, then take his subspecialty training. He will be a successful M.D. If his parents were poor, he will rise in the social establishment.

He will be a success. But will he ever become a physician? Has he been called? Will he ever discover that he has or has not been called? Has he chosen the healing path—or only a convenient career as an M.D.? Only the future can answer those questions.

There is for some souls a moment in life when the decision is made, a moment (usually unknown to anyone) when that person is set on the healer's life-path. In my own life, that moment came when I was six years old, but I didn't realize it until I was nearly seventy.

One spring day I was playing on the sidewalk in front of my house when another little boy came up the sidewalk carrying a shoebox. The boy took the lid off the shoebox, and inside the box were three little guinea pigs. One was white, one was brown, and one was checkered brown and black and white.

I wanted one of those guinea pigs for myself! The little boy said he was selling them for a quarter apiece. I ran into the house and yelled for Mom and begged a quarter so I could buy a guinea pig. Mom gave me a quarter and I ran out and bought the beautiful little checkered guinea pig.

I had never had a pet of my own before and this one was my very own. I kept him in a shoebox on the back porch and punched holes in the lid of the box for air, and I fed him lettuce and watched him nibble the lettuce and I was very proud, very happy.

But the next day, when I took the lid off the box, the guinea pig jumped out and skidded across the porch and down the wooden stairs and began to run away. I chased him as fast as I could run. The guinea pig kept close to the walls of the house and up under the bushes where he couldn't be reached; and I chased him at top speed until he was really out of breath.

Finally I saw him stop running. I ran up to him and kneeled down to pick him up. The little guinea pig was spreadeagled with his nose in the dirt and his four little paws spread out and he was panting in total exhaustion. I realized that I had chased him too hard. He looked as if he might die at any moment.

The thought flashed through my mind that I had broken my guinea pig.

I felt a feeling through my whole body that I had never felt before, a mixture of shame and grief and remorse and fear and a desire to undo what I had done and a realization that I had unknowingly exceeded the tolerance limits of the little creature that meant so much to me. I picked him up and gently carried him back to the shoebox and gave him some fresh lettuce and let him rest.

Gradually his panting subsided, and he returned to normal. But for me the world had changed forever. You must care for what you love or you will lose it.

THE PHANTOM BEDWETTING ALARM[20]

Have you ever seen that bedwetter's alarm device that you buy at the store? You rig it up with a battery and the alarm goes off the instant a drop of moisture touches the sheet. I explained how it works to an eight-year-old boy whose parents had been fighting for years and were about to get a divorce. He had been wetting the bed for several years.

I explained to him in detail how the alarm works.

Some months later I again saw the parents and asked them how well the device had worked. They had never used it. They never even bought one. He had stopped wetting the bed the very same night of the day that I explained to him in detail how the alarm works.

After all, the boy had already had the experience, created in his mind by my words, of being waked by a buzzer at the instant of feeling his bladder muscle relax. He was cured by an imaginary bedwetting alarm. I call it the phantom bedwetting alarm.

---

20 Reported in *Elegant Parenting*, 1994

THE PROM DRESS

Carol A. Gall

Every Sunday afternoon John and I held parenting classes in the large conference room at the back of the office. It was furnished with soft couches and many large pillows, perfect for settling in for the two hours of our meetings together. Along the back wall of the conference room there were large windows looking out over a large expanse of land which sloped downward to a small forest. Occasionally deer would gaze at us and birds of all kinds would warble their calls. In winter the red feathers of the male cardinals added the clarion call of color; in spring we delighted in their earnest calls seeking mates. Every species displays the best of itself, it seems, during the mating season.

Our group was not inordinately large, though sometimes we had as many as thirty. Other times we would have as few as eight or ten. Mostly it was the mothers who came to listen to John and me share our insights. Husbands were welcome, too, but it was mostly the women who arrived to explore together with us concepts that might help them in the day-to- day task of parenting their children. Some parents said they welcomed the relief from their children that our meetings provided, as their tots were left with babysitters for the duration of our meetings. For some of these children, Sunday afternoons meant a special time alone with Dad, or with grandparents.

We had certain ground rules for the meetings. One of the most important was that we stayed on parenting topics in a general sense. The meetings were not meant to focus on any one family's personal issues, marital problems, physical problems, and the like. We wanted to provide context and meaning for issues that all parents faced. Of course, families could and did provide examples of problems and solutions in their personal experience, but we were not a therapy group, per se.

One Sunday, however, all of our good intentions regarding ground rules were of no avail.

Janine was upset. Janine had been coming to the parenting classes since their inception, nearly, and was an expert at applying the ideas to her own children and to the children in large day care she ran in her home. When others were questioning what actions to take with their children, she often spoke up with just the right modicum of common sense and innovation. She was especially attuned to the need for parents to get out alone, away from their children. She could sense when another parent was experiencing problems with his or her children, not because of any lack of skill or love on their part, but from pure burn-out.

She would echo my husband's famous words, saying, "You need to get out! Go out to dinner once a week. Don't tell the children where you are going! Only your babysitter needs to know where you are! They need to know that you have a life that doesn't involve them! They need to know that you are separate people whose happiness does not depend on them! You will lift their burden as well as yours if you convey that separateness to them!"

This Sunday, however, Janine was furious with her daughter. She said to the group in her rarely heard angry and exasperated voice, "Melinda insists on buying a dress for the senior prom that costs a hundred and fifty dollars! We have too many children for that! She simply can't spend that kind of money for a dress she will wear once, maybe twice! Does anyone have any suggestions for how I should handle her outrageous craving for extravagance?"

Marlys spoke up saying, "Why don't you let her earn her own money to pay for the dress!"

Janine said, "Oh, it's not that she doesn't have the money. She has the money saved for the dress from her babysitting jobs."

Marlys said, "Then why don't you let her have the dress if she is able to improve in one of her classes, or if she studies more?"

Janine scowled. "Melinda is an A student. That incentive would not work. Anyway, it is not a question of responsibility in that way. She has a full academic scholarship for her freshman year of college. It's not about personal responsibility except in this one way. She wants to waste a hundred and fifty dollars on one dress! I am furious with her!"

My husband and I let the class grapple with Janine and Melinda's problem for nearly two hours. The prom dress was the topic of conversation even when we broke for fifteen minutes for coffee and cookies. Strategy after strategy was suggested to Janine by other parents, but Janine was as frustrated, angry, and distraught as when she had first arrived.

When the class began to break up I asked Janine if she was in a hurry. "Would you mind staying for a moment after everyone leaves?" She said, "I can do that!"

It took fifteen minutes for everyone to say their last good-byes. John and I had noticed that certain parents liked to linger, liked to have more of a private conversation with one or the other of us. Usually these conversations were more social than information seeking, but important to the parents involved. We enjoyed that ending camaraderie as much as the parents seemed to.

Janine waited patiently. When everyone had left, I asked her to go with me into a small conference room that we kept for the convenience of nursing mothers. I motioned for her to sit down in the wooden rocking chair. Janine rocked back and forth for a bit as I studied her face, trying to choose my words carefully.

Finally I said, "Janine, do you ever wear a dress?" I had never seen her in a dress, either at her children's appointments, in a parenting class, or around town.

Janine replied, "No, I don't."

I asked her gently, "Janine, were you ever sexually abused as a child?"

Her hand flew to her mouth and she gasped. "Oh!" she declared. "It's not Melinda's problem! It's my problem! She can have the dress!"

Janine and I became friends and still keep in touch. I wanted to write her story for this book, but didn't feel comfortable about it without her permission. I called her and recounted the entire incident to her.

Much to my surprise Janine said, "I have no memory whatsoever of that particular class!"

I said, "I have it all on tape!"

Janine said, "If you had written that story and I had read your book, I would have thought, 'What a crazy lady!' Go ahead and use it!"

My husband, however, was not surprised when I told him of our conversation. "Often when an issue becomes a non-issue, people forget completely about it. It means you have had a success!" He smiled at me tenderly as he said it and I wondered if I would ever be as wise as he.

THE WORDS TO SAY IT

Up to the age of eight or nine months, babies have the power to reproduce any sound in any language. They can learn Mandarin, Hindi, or Urdu as easily as English, and they can speak it without an accent. They also make up words of their own to refer to things of interest to themselves.

The eight-month-old boy sitting on my examining table was obviously enjoying the exam. He smiled when I used my ophthalmoscope to look in his eyes, and he stared right back into the light.

"Rrrgh!" he said as he grabbed for the instrument.

"Rrrgh!" I replied as I evaded his grasp. "Do you want my light? Light! Light!"

"Rrrgh!"

I gave him the light and he proceeded to wave it in my face, repeating, "Rrrgh!"

Suddenly I understood. "Rrrgh!" was his own word for the instrument. I pointed to it and repeated, "Rrrgh! Rrrgh! Rrrgh!"

He exploded with joy and enthusiasm, waving the ophthalmoscope at me and repeating, "Rrrgh! Rrrgh! Rrrgh!"

A few weeks later his mother brought him in again. I could hardly believe my eyes. His posture was slumped, he failed to make eye contact, and when he looked up, there was a darkness in his eyes that gave me a pang. He made no sound, but watched me with those dark eyes.

"What happened?" I asked his mother.

She replied, "I have just learned that his babysitter has been spanking him."

She removed his diaper. His buttocks were black and blue.

"This woman is a grandmother. I confronted her, and she told me that it was her duty to spank him in order to drive the devil out of him. I argued with her and she insisted. I told her she was through as a babysitter."

The mother pressed charges against the babysitter and took her to court. In open court the babysitter defended herself by saying that she was only doing her duty, and that she would continue to spank any baby entrusted to her, in order to drive out the devil.

THIRTY-THREE EYE PATCHES[21]

Heidi had a lazy eye and came home from the eye doctor with a patch over her good eye. She was really upset about having to go to daycare with an eye patch. When she got to the daycare she found thirty-three kids running around with patches on their eyes. She was the happiest girl in the world!

The teachers did it. While Heidi was at the doctor's office, they proceeded to cut out patches and have every kid at the daycare wear a patch. Heidi was as happy as can be and wore that patch for the next 6 months.

They only did it for the one day. They never needed to do it again.

---

21 Original story in *Dancing with Elves*, 2000.

WART BE GONE

She was eleven years old and she had a nasty wart in her right armpit. She had put a bandaid on it to hide it. She loosened one end of the bandaid to show me the wart. It was dark and it looked like a big mole.

I explained to her mother that there were a number of ways to treat a nasty wart. She seemed interested and I talked a little longer than I usually do, feeling inwardly just a little self-satisfied to be able to speak with authority on a common pediatric subject.

I talked about Huck Finn and Tom Sawyer and collecting spunk-water at midnight from a rotting tree-stump.

"Sometimes they even fall off on their own accord," I said.

A movement from the girl caught my attention.

"Look," she said. "It's falling off!"

As I watched, the wart fell free of her armpit. There was no scar.

A little dazed, they left without a prescription.

WHAT DID THE DOCTOR SAY?

Carol Gall

Sometimes my husband had very bad news to tell parents. If I were not already in the office, he would call me to come in to be with him and the parents, so that together we could digest what this bad news would mean to the patient and to the family. My husband found my presence comforting, and some parents appreciated the presence of a woman, a mother, in the room. For a conversation like this, we sat not in the examining room, but in the large room in the back of the office, with its comfortable chairs and its coffee pot. We closed the big double doors for privacy; the staff knew not to interrupt us when the doors were shut.

A father had brought his three-year-old son in to be seen by my husband because the child had a sore throat. My husband suspected immediately that there was much more going on than a sore throat and his worst suspicions were confirmed with a simple lab test. This little boy was diabetic and would be insulin dependent the rest of his life.

Treatment needed to commence immediately. Mother was not there to hear the news. Carefully my husband explained to the father that his son's pancreas was not producing enough insulin, that his son had the disease we call diabetes. Because this was the first time the condition had made itself known, he would need to be evaluated. This evaluation would take one week of hospitalization, and would be conducted at the hospital. The father nodded his head, indicating that he was listening and understanding.

University Hospital is a very large complex. My husband drew a map of how to get to the correct spot to park. He drew another map of exactly how to get to the correct check-in desk. The father and my husband shook hands and the father left holding hands with his son.

We were both very saddened as we sat eating our lunch. The telephone rang, and I got up to answer it. It was the boy's father.

"What did Dr. Gall say my son has? What did he tell us to do?"

I gave the phone to my husband who patiently repeated all that he had previously said.

Sometimes bad news is like bad food—impossible to digest.

WHAT WAS THAT?

He was a delicate eight year old boy, an only child, whose prominent and imposing parents chose to bring him into my practice because of his precarious health. In order that I might be fully apprised of his medical condition, they had prepared a ten-page typewritten summary, single-spaced, starting with details of mother's pregnancy, the delivery, and each and every well-baby checkup. To make sure I understood, they read it to me from beginning to end.

Among the many diagnoses his parents had discovered in their child, one stood out. He had recently begun to suffer from asthma. What caught my attention was the fact that he had recently made three trips in three weeks to the emergency room for severe asthmatic attacks.

I decided to examine him without his parents present. They were happy to be spared the need of another doctor visit, but warned me that they would seek a second medical opinion if they were not satisfied with my management of the case.

I discovered a small, delicately-built eight-year-old boy whose lungs were perfectly clear.

I surmised that he felt cornered by his massive, meticulous parents who were obviously devoting their entire attention to this only child.

After the exam, on a hunch, I said to him, forcefully, with great emphasis, "I know what you are doing and I want you to stop it!"

He grinned, a rueful, rather secretive grin, and never had another asthmatic attack. Instead, he began to grow. With each passing year he became bigger and more rugged, until he was even more massive than his parents. By age eighteen, I joked with him that he must shave with a chain saw.

He played football in high school and then joined the Marines.

WHAT'S IN A NAME?

Carol A. Gall

When my husband, John, and I married, I moved from St. Paul, Minnesota, to Michigan, to join him and to work in his pediatric office.

Our town had many professionals, both men and women. Partly because so many women had married later in life and established careers with their given names, and partly because of a sense that women needed their separate identities apart from men, large numbers of women kept their given names, or as some would say, their maiden names. This meant that when I was trying to memorize the names of my husband's friends as well as his patients' names, I had to know the father's last name *and* the mother's last name.

However, it was more than learning just two sets of names, because some families gave their children the last name of the father, some gave the last name of the mother, others had hyphenated names using the surnames of both parents, but one couldn't infer which surname came first, and others gave the boys the last name of their fathers, but the girls the last name of their mothers.

It was a daunting task for me, and I worked hard at it every day. It surprised me that when parents called to make appointments for their children, they did not automatically supply all the information I needed right when they called. When Mary Marsten called to make an appointment for her daughter, Belinda, if I didn't recall her husband's last name, Kirkegaard, or the particular mode for naming they had chosen, I could waste lots of times looking for a chart. Yet, some mothers resented being asked.

John and I frequented a market that would have been an outdoor market, we supposed, except that the Michigan winter meant that four walls and a modicum of heat were necessary to keep the produce from freezing. It was less than elegant, but had tasty, often organic produce. We bought most of our fruits, vegetables, and nuts there.

One Saturday morning after John had fulfilled his hospital duties, we went together to this market to purchase our produce. We were filling our basket with goods and talking to one another, when my husband got a peculiar look on his face. He looked down, and so did I, to see a little boy three years old hanging onto his pants leg. When John had taken his last step, the little boy had been lifted up in the air with John's leg, and back down.

He had a mischievous look on his face when my husband looked down at him and the tot grinned broadly, obviously happy to see my husband. The two of them chatted a moment, then the mother noticed that her child had left her side, and walked to us. When he saw his mother, the child let go of John's pants, but stood beside him happily. John said to the Mom, "This is my wife, Carol!" but didn't mention the woman's name and she didn't volunteer it.

I was deep into memorizing names, so when we got into the car I asked John, "What is the name of the little boy that hung onto your pants leg?"

He said, "When he was born, he was jaundiced. He had to be under the lights. Little babies are born with an excess of hemoglobin, which was needed in utero, but needs to be broken down after birth. Some babies' livers are too immature to do this work, since the enzyme, which is present in the liver at birth, is present in a small quantity. The liver needs to manufacture more enzyme to break down the excess hemoglobin, and sometimes the liver is unable to do this efficiently enough to get rid of the excess. This can cause cerebral palsy. It is important that the baby get under the lights, which speeds up the process of this breakdown."

I not only had to memorize names, I had to memorize medical procedures and their reasons. My brain was on overdrive.

"What is the little boy's name?" I repeated.

He said, "When he was fifteen months old he tripped and cut his forehead on the coffee table. We put a bandaid on it."

I said again, "The name, John, what is his name"?

He said, "When he was two he had several ear infections and ran a high fever. His mother was quite worried about him, but they got through it okay."

Exasperated now I said loudly, "*The name, John! What is his name?*"

He said, "I have no idea!"

Doctors have peculiar minds, I decided, but it was better that he remembered the relevant medical information than the name.

WHEN TO SIGN

We all know that some handicaps are terribly real, terribly final. What we *don't* know is how much of a particular handicap is irreducible.

Little Demetria was born with several strikes against her. She suffered from intrauterine growth retardation, weighing only 5 pounds 2 ounces at birth. She exhibited small head size and cerebral palsy. She was soon diagnosed with congenital cytomegalovirus infection. But long before anyone had made this diagnosis, her mother had noticed, at the early age of three months, that Demetria wasn't responding properly to sounds.

She took her to a hearing specialist who discovered that Demetria had sensorineural deafness. She was almost totally deaf. There was no trace of hearing in the left ear, and there was only a suggestion of response in the right ear at the boost level of 80 decibels.

Demetria's mother decided not to wait. She began teaching Demetria sign language, and at twelve months of age she enrolled Demetria in the local county hearing-impaired program.

It was slow going. By nineteen months of age Demetria could only understand four signs and perform two signs.

But then something happened. By thirty-four months she could sign and understand over 150 signs, and four months after that she was signing and understanding over 300 signs. She was no longer being called developmentally delayed.

At three and a half years she was reading, and at five and a half years she was in Kindergarten doing very well, working on math concepts, reading, and spelling.

Demetria's mother saved her own child from a lifetime of mental retardation. I didn't have anything to do with it except to encourage her in the crazy project of teaching a three-month-old infant to learn sign language.

HE DIDN'T KNOW WHEN TO WAKE UP[22]

(A verbatim transcript from a parenting class conducted by John and Beth Gall)

BG: We had one little kid who wouldn't go to sleep at night, wouldn't even go to bed at night. This went on for weeks, and the parents were exhausted.

JG: He didn't fit any of the common patterns, he wasn't going to sleep and then waking up and demanding the presence of the parents, and he wasn't hungry, and he wasn't afraid of his room.

BG: He wasn't afraid of the dark.

JG: He wasn't afraid of the dark, he wasn't afraid of being separated from his parents. But he just wouldn't sleep. He would not put his head down and go to sleep.

BG: We suggested several things, like having the dog sleep in the room. Well, the dog didn't like that. They had trouble with the dog! The dog couldn't sleep!

JG: Ordinarily that's a marvelous solution because the dog is such good company.

BG: Anyway, they had a neighbor in to baby-sit one night. They were getting pretty exhausted and needed to get out for an evening. The neighbor, who was a grandmother age person, finally figured it out. She said, "Maybe he doesn't know when he has to get up,"—because the mother worked and everybody had to get out of the house in the morning. "Maybe he's afraid he isn't going to get up in the morning on time."

JG: He was afraid that he might be asleep when it was time to go.

BG: So they gave him a windup alarm clock, and they set

---
22 From *Elegant Parenting*, 1994

it so that it would go off at 6:30 in the morning. They showed him how it would work and what it sounded like, and they told him, "When you hear this bell, then you get up. That's time to get up and get ready for the day."

That solved the problem completely! He would go in his bed, they'd do the ritual of setting the clock, and he'd put his head down and go off to sleep, with great security, knowing that he would be waked up in time. He hadn't told anybody that. He hadn't been able to express that. He was only about three, I guess. The babysitter, from the outside looking in, made one guess and it happened to be a pretty good one.

Arthur: It's like the night before vacation or a big test or something. Waking up to look at the clock to make sure you don't oversleep.

BG: The problem was exactly the opposite of what it seemed to be. He didn't want to go to sleep because he was afraid he wouldn't wake up at the right time.

JG: There's that, "Ah-ha!" experience when you realize, "Oh, this is not that. This is not that, this is this."

WHY NOT LEARN TO FLY THE REAL THING?[23]

Our son David had been an avid model airplane enthusiast ever since the age of seven. When he got to be fourteen, he said, "I want a motorcycle." He had already taken a used car apart and left it in the backyard.

We were thinking, "Oh, my God. Another motorcycle bum."

Then my wife did this amazing thing, just on the spur of the moment. She said, "What do you want to mess around with motorcycles for? You've been a model airplane builder all your life. Why don't you learn to fly the real thing?"

She said, "I'll take you down to Willow Run and we'll do a trial flight today, right now."

She drove this fourteen year old out to Willow Run on the spur of the moment, located the pilot and said, "My son wants to fly!"

She sat out on the tarmac and watched.

Half an hour went by, the time was up for the five dollars, forty-five minutes, fifty minutes, an hour—and she began to wonder, where did they go? Did they crash?

Then the plane appeared and began to wobble back towards the airport and wobblingly circled the airport and wobblingly came down and bounced a little bit and came to a stop and—out jumped David!

"Mom, I flew it! I flew it!"

There never was any talk again about motorcycles. He was going to be an airplane pilot. And that's just how it turned out.

---

23 Reported in *Elegant Parenting*, 1994.

WON'T PLAY BALL

It's hard now, looking back, to realize how things were then, before the discovery of child abuse.

He was four years old. His father, the police chief of the neighboring town, thought he might be retarded because he didn't want to play ball with his father. He spent all his time indoors, playing quietly or just staring into space. He seldom spoke. He yelped, a monotonous, barking yelp. His father whipped him conscientiously with his belt at least once a week, but that didn't seem to help. In fact, things seemed to be getting worse. He was yelping more often, sometimes spontaneously between whippings.

I sent him for psychological testing and met with his father again.

"His IQ is 140," I said. "He's gifted. You need to buy him some children's books, get him a teacher, send him to Kindergarten."

"No way," said his father. "If he starts school early, when he gets to High School he won't have his full growth and he won't be able to play on the football team."

WON'T SLEEP IN HER CRIB[24]

She was the baby no one thought would make it here. When she came—three weeks premature—she actually weighed over six pounds and Mom lived, as she said, "in fear that her real mother would show up and claim her." Her story follows:

I can't get this child to sleep *whatsoever* in her crib.

I wanted to be a breastfeeding Mom. She literally refused to feed for eight weeks. So I used a breast pump and fed her breast milk for eight weeks. Then I tried the formula again. Two bottles of formula—and she decided she would rather breast feed!

Part of the advice of the lactation consultant was to put her in bed with us—to feed her in the bed with the two of us, which really worked well. And now she doesn't want the bottle. But now she wants to keep sleeping there, in the bed with us.

So I moved her from there to the car seat, which she loves. She'll sleep in the car seat as much as ten hours. But she will not go at all into her crib. She will not sleep in the crib. She wakes up every hour. The car seat—she will sleep in. The crib—she won't sleep in. She'll cry for an hour, until I put her in her seat.

I've been told by a number of people, "She needs to sleep in her bed! You need to let her cry!"

People have said, "She's just manipulating you! You need to make her give this up! You need to insist!" But she's very unhappy when I do that!

I asked her if she would be willing to continue with the present arrangement.

---

24 This interview can be viewed online at www.higherlevelparenting.com at Section II, Chapter 21, Module 5, "No Crib."

Yes. I guess I'd like to know, somewhere down the line, that she will go in her crib and be comfortable sleeping there. She's getting bigger, and I don't want her to spend her whole childhood in the car seat.

But I'm afraid that I'm allowing her to have a habit, that she will not transition well and—

"They're scaring you," I said.

Yes. And—this is the baby I thought I'd never have, and I wonder if I'm not being very firm with her, and if I'm not— for a long time I didn't want to give her up. I didn't want her to sleep in her crib! And I wonder if I've created this problem.

I told her I didn't think she created the problem at all.

Is there any issue with her sleeping in the car seat—her posture, or anything?

I told her, "No. It's OK. The way to get a kid through a stage is to let them get their fill of it."

Long silence.

And eventually—?

Eventually she will get bored with this because she has moved on to the next higher level.

Well, I have to be honest and say that that's not what's been sort of beat over my head. My previous doctor kept saying, "She *needs* to do this, she *needs* to do that." But she's not! And so I'm putting her in this crib—she doesn't want to sleep in there—and she's waking up every hour, just crying. I'm waking up every hour with her. She's unhappy, I don't want her to be crying, and the doctor—"Oh, she needs to sleep in her own bed. This is the time when sleeping patterns are established. She needs to go in the bed! You'll have her twelve years old! Put her in there and let her cry!"

You could do that, but it's pretty hard!

Well, let me tell you, I tried to get this baby to breast feed for eight weeks, and she—we had all the best lactation consultants, and this one consultant said, "I will put this baby to breast!" She stayed for three hours, and the baby didn't do it. And the lady walked out and said, "You have a very intelligent baby who is very stubborn!"

I suggested that this is not stubbornness, it's determination.

And she didn't do it until she was ready! This little girl is only four months old, and I feel that she's already got the will of iron! She's going to do exactly what she wants to do!

And aren't you glad!

Well, she's the baby who held on!

Right! She held on! That's why she's here!

She held on! She was determined to be here. And she's generally extremely happy. I don't have any problems with her in any direction. But I'm worried—and I guess her Dad is also—that, "Well, I bought this crib for her, and it's her bed, and she should sleep in her bed."

But the question is, how does she view the bed, not how does Dad view the bed!

Well, what will happen? Do you think—

She's going to grow up to be a very assertive, strong-willed, well-balanced person. And your greatest gift to her would be to let her know that she can get those things that she wants, as long as it's not dangerous to life or limb.

And you don't feel that this—just let her sleep in her seat and that's OK?

The way she wants it!

Rolling up all these blankets! I tell you, every single night I go through this. It seems like a small issue, but—she doesn't want to sleep there! And I have done everything from—elevate the bed—all kinds of things, and everyone's pushing me to tell her to sleep there, and—she sleeps fine in the seat, she sleeps through the night in her seat.

And that's a great place for a baby to sleep! Is it going to make a problem if you start telling the folks that you are under orders to do it the other way?

No, I guess what I feel is, I would like her to sleep where she can sleep the best, as long as I'm not creating a problem for her by allowing something that's not going to be—

That's not going to happen! It will be over some other issue, like using the family car!

I'm a teacher, and I feel like I see a lot of kids at twelve who—are—brats, and their parents have not become their parents, and I just don't want to do that. But now I'm looking at her, and I think—

This is not a brat!

She's not a brat!

No, she's not a brat! She's simply asserting what you and I would call civil rights.

And very determined—like, "I will do—" and you can just see it in her face. How a baby this little could be that determined! But she's very determined, and if she doesn't want something, she's not going to do it. And this is creating a lot of stress in the family, because—

In whom?

Well, between my husband and me and her, because the doctor has told us we have to do this.

Oh, it's really the doctor that created this stress!

Well, yes! I was saying that she was sleeping with us, and the doctor was saying, "Don't do that! You'll never get her out of the bed!"

Oh, but you can! You can get her out of the bed later on! The way to raise any baby, but especially a baby like this, is to ask them what they want—*and then do it! And if it isn't a matter of life and limb, that's fine. If it's a matter of life and limb, you just do otherwise. But on stuff where they've got the final say, like sleeping or eating, you don't tell them what to do, you ask them what they want to do.*

And she's made that very clear. I don't have any question in my mind where she would like to sleep.

You know, when she gets older, she's going to be so grateful to you for making the way easy.

Well, I'd just rather do it that way. I never felt so powerfully responsible, like—am I creating a problem?

This idea that a kid will rigidly do for the next eighty-seven years what they are doing as a four-monther—that's a strange idea! People change. As they get older they want different things.

And she hasn't consistently done the same thing for the past four months, ever.

No, she hasn't!

But she loves her chair. I can put it in her room. I've put it in her bed. I've put it just about everywhere, and that's where she's the most content.

That's her security. Don't take away her security!

(Long silence)

So this is OK?

This is OK!

And then do I just gradually, at some point, as she grows out of this—

She'll tell you! You won't have to ask her. She'll tell you.

The day will come when she will look at that thing and she'll say, "Uh-uh!"

"It's not comfortable any more?"

Right! And of course, if you want to help that process along, you can let her stay in it until she's a little too big for it.

She has grown, and I'd love at some point to weigh her. She seems like she has grown overwhelmingly, from a baby that was barely six pounds two ounces, and I look at her and—

She's got that life drive in her.

And she eats what she wants to eat. And I never thought she'd get here. And I keep thinking, "Please don't have this baby's real mother come pick her up!" This just feels like it can't be real. And she's not a child who cries for anything unless she's upset. And to put her in that crib every night and listen to that.

And deliberately upset her.

And know that she's not going to make it through the night, not going to sleep through. And I was worried with her sleeping in the bed with us just because I felt like—she almost fell off a couple of times. But to have her in the seat—we all sleep!

Everybody sleeps. She's happy, you're happy!

Right! And I'd just as soon do that.

Right! Here is the answer, right here, and there are people who don't want to take it, like doctors and well-meaning advisors, and so forth.

Well, there was that indication that in the future there will be harm because of this.

There is fear for the future.

And, "You're allowing this baby to create a very, very bad habit. She needs to know that there are places to sleep, and a car seat is not one of them!"

They are going to try to teach a four month old that they should do this and not that?

Well, we had four adults at one time, trying to get this baby to breast feed, and it didn't work. We had four very educated people!

That's right! She decides!

And she decided when she was ready, and then it was easy!

Isn't it fun? Once you get to where you can read their signals. And they will tell you. It's so plain! And then you just do what they say.

Um-hmm.

That's how you "control" them!

Well, I'm sure it sounds like I'm making a much bigger problem out of this than it is, but—it has been a problem. It's been a very big problem for us, because I've constantly put her in this bed, and she doesn't want to go in there. And I don't want her to be "dysfunctional." Why are we already saying that word to a four month old?

That's borrowing trouble.

Well, they said, when they came to tape her—this lactation consultant, they said, "Well, we want a tape of this dysfunctional breast feeder."

Oh, no! That's ridiculous!

And she wasn't feeding then.

This is not a dysfunctional breast feeder! This is a kid who decided for a while that she didn't want to.

And she just waited. And all this "nipple confusion" and "if you give her a bottle she won't take it"—

I don't believe in that.

No! that's nonsense!

She had nothing but a bottle for two months, and now she knows how to breast feed just fine! And she knows she doesn't want the formula now.

Right! And she knows how to sleep in another place, in another posture, when she's ready.

And that will be OK?

And that will be OK!

Well, I'd just like to let go of that.

(The child, having nursed her fill, is asleep in Mom's arms.)

This kid sleeps great!

This is my baby from heaven. She's got a smile so big it doesn't fit on her face. It's just—

It's going to be real easy to raise her because you just notice what she wants, and then do that.

And that's OK to do?

That is perfectly OK. That's what every adult wants, isn't it?

(Mother laughs) Well, I think maybe I need to be educated on this.

Well, you've got a lot of people around you who are coming from the standard, traditional child-development standpoint. And you know, a lot of this comes from Germany.

This attitude, or—?

This child development approach—that the child has to be taught what they should do at two months and four months and six months.

And they really don't need it at all?

That's German, yeah.

So, we can discontinue it?

Drop it!

Well, maybe I just need to be educated about—

Just dance with her!

Well, that's a lot less complicated.

One more thing. I'm worrying about whether your biggest problem is going to be with the people who give you the advice.

It does feel like my heart tells me one thing, but I want to trust other people who have all that education, and when somebody with a lot of experience and a lot of degrees tells you what to do—

Would it help if you told them—I don't know, maybe you can level with your husband about it—but you can tell them that you have been to see me and that we're working on it, and that my recommendations for the time being are that you not change anything, that we feel that she needs some time to stabilize in the present situation.

I'm very happy to do that. In fact, I've tried to make this point and ask questions. Now I was concerned about her not breast feeding and I wanted to feed her and I said something to her doctor—her previous doctor—and I said I really wanted her to be a breast feeder, and it was, "Well, she's not! She's not going to be, so give her the bottle. She'll still go to college." And I just can't deal with that response.

It's too pat! Too brief!

So I've tried to stay with it, and I've tried to go with it, and I've had too much hassle about it. So I just called today. "I need to find a new pediatrician." So I don't have those people as my advisors any more!

All right!

WRINKLY CHICKEN[25]

Susanna and Leora were just two years apart in age, and they worked as a team to frustrate Mom. They just didn't like the way their food was served at mealtime.

They wouldn't eat their sandwich because it wasn't cut just exactly in the middle.

They wouldn't drink their juice because the two glasses weren't just exactly equally full. They even refused delicious fried chicken because the skin was all wrinkly.

My wife had previously suggested that the parents tape-record their mealtimes and then just listen to the tape—in the privacy of their own home, of course—after the kids had gone to bed. They reported back in class that it was even more horrible than they remembered—constant bickering and arguing about food and eating. Mealtimes sometimes lasted an hour, even two hours. Arguing about eating had expanded to fill up their waking life.

(By the way, that's the value of a tape recording—it gives you feedback about how you sound to the kids, about how you really are interacting with them.)

To Mom's consternation, I agreed with the girls that they really ought not to eat such food. I suggested to Mom that she continue to prepare it as she always had done, but at the last moment of offering it she was to jerk it back and discover the flaw for herself:

"Oh! I'm sorry, this sandwich isn't cut right. You won't want this. I'm going to throw it away."

"Oh! I'm sorry, this chicken is all wrinkly. You don't want this. I'll put it away."

And what happened? We had to wait a week for the next parenting class. The parents reported an incredible turnaround.

25 Reported in *Elegant Parenting*, 1994

When Mom started to take the food away, the two girls cried out together,

"We'll eat it, we'll eat it!"

Being trained psychologists, the parents saw they were on to a good thing and so they extended their new method to almost everything.

"It's cold outside this morning, but you won't want your coat. I'll just put it back in the closet!"

"No, Mom! We'll wear it. We'll wear it!"

And after supper: "It's too late to do your homework tonight. You'll just have to leave it undone!"

"No, Mom! We'll do it!"

And that was the end of that problem. The two girls were still working together as a team to frustrate Mom and Dad, but whenever they won their argument they ended up doing what Mom and Dad wanted.

WRITE TO ME!

Carol A. Gall

One year I was invited to teach a group of about fifteen mildly mentally retarded young men and women who were housed in a junior high school in a mostly rich suburb of the Twin Cities. The idea of having such young people in a school and segregating them in order to better fulfill their special needs was a new idea at that time. In earlier years such students had simply languished in schools if they were of a placid type. Or if they weren't, especially if they were frustrated and expressed their frustration by "acting out," the response of the school systems was to find a reason to get rid of them. In short, they were expelled.

My year of teaching began with an attempt on my part to see just where their abilities waxed, and where they waned. Their ages ranged from twelve to seventeen and I assumed they had as varying levels of achievement as their varied ages would imply.

I handed out worksheets to try to determine just what they knew and what they didn't. I encountered a problem I was not expecting. For the most part, I couldn't read a word of what they had written on their papers.

I encouraged them to write legibly, and handed out a different set of worksheets with the same results. After this happened three or four times, I admitted defeat. "There is no way I can read your papers!"

Several in the group protested, saying, "But we are doing our very best! We are just not very good at writing!"

Aha. A light came on. "Okay, if cursive writing is hard for you, why don't you try printing?"

The group was eager to please me with another try, so I prepared another batch of worksheets. Unfortunately, I found their printing to be nearly as impossible to read as their cursive writing. I was exasperated.

A few days went by with no thought of how to solve this problem. Yes, I could order them penmanship booklets in which they could practice their handwriting, but certainly we couldn't work on that all day long, and orders submitted had to go through a process. First there was the requisition, then the approval process, then the order submission followed by the wait for the materials to arrive. When they would arrive, they had to be checked by the central receiving center, loaded onto a truck and then, finally, delivered to the school, checked again by the school's ordering section, after which they would finally reach me. Obviously, this was not a simple or quick process.

It took me a couple of days to come up with an idea.

If I were going to see what my students were able to do, I would give them a challenge. I rose from my desk and walked to the adjacent chalkboard.

I announced, "I am going to write your assignments and anything else I need to write on the chalkboard with my left hand. I don't usually use my left hand, so I am going to print. I won't be very good at it. I hope you can read it!"

I wrote a sentence on the board. A few students tittered softly as they viewed my very flawed attempt, a few more joined in, and soon all the students were laughing out loud at my pitiful attempts to use my left hand.

They said, "Your writing is *too hard* to read!"

I said, "I'm sorry, but that is the best I can do. I am trying as hard as I can. But if you wish, we can all try to improve. I will continue to write on the chalkboard with my left hand. I will try very hard to write so that you can read my left hand writing. I will do that if you will try your hardest to write with your usual writing hand so that I can read your papers.

The class accepted the challenge. By the end of the year their handwriting was magnificent and I had mastered the art of printing on the chalkboard with my left hand, a skill I retain to this day if the chalk is the same size as I had then. (Writing is a very specific skill.)

My husband calls this strategy "going one down to go one up." It works well in numerous settings with adults and children alike. If you think of ways to use this strategy, please write to me—legibly, of course!

Other publications by the same author, available directly from General Systemantics Press (please add $7.50 for shipping and handling):

Elegant Parenting. Strategies for the Twenty-first Century
978-0-9618251-3-3 $37.50

Dancing with Elves. Parenting as a Performing Art
978-0-9618251-4-0 $13.95

The Systems Bible (3d edition of Systemantics)
978-0-9618251-7-1 $27.95

First Queen. A Historical Novel on the Life of Hatshepsut Queen of Egypt
978-0-9618251-6-4 $37.50

HLP-DVD (The parenting program entitled Higher Level Parenting, on DVD)
$20.00

Order online from our web site at www.generalsystemantics. com or directly from General Systemantics Press (check or money order only, please) at: 7027 S. Walker Bay Road, NW, Walker, MN 56484.